Advance Praise for *Campaigning for Cl—*

Meredith A...
Pro Nuclear...
a nuclear ad\...
is a primer fo...
and education...

... for
... as
... book
... ascinating guidebook

— Thomas P. Salmon
Governor of Vermont (1972–1977)

Turning enthusiasm into organized, responsible advocacy, Meredith Angwin has been on the forefront of nuclear advocacy for years and she shares her experiences and lessons learned. This is far more than a "how-to manual"; it is a life's journey into greater understanding of how to responsibly address public concerns over nuclear power or any technically complex issue.

— Dr. Dale E. Klein, Former Chairman,
U.S. Nuclear Regulatory Commission

At last—a practical, clearly voiced guidebook to approaching nuclear power. I heartily endorse Meredith Angwin's important guidebook about how to talk about the cleanest and safest source of base-load power we have. A scientist and a communications expert, her writing is direct and natural, flows well, and speaks directly to how people wishing to better support nuclear power can learn to spread the word.

— Gwyneth Cravens, author of *Power to Save the World: The Truth About Nuclear Energy*

I must first thank Meredith for her courage and strength. Her vast knowledge of the nuclear industry and team-building experience is evident here.

For too long, attacks on the nuclear industry have gone unanswered. The measures described in this book are not based on looking at the conflict from outside. To combat the guerilla tactics used by antinuclear groups, Angwin has been involved directly, even organizing demonstrations on the sidewalks of Brattleboro, Vermont. Now, she uses her pen to bring you an excellent organizational toolkit. Her work is suited for a broad audience, and it will help propel our community into directed action.

— George Clain
President and Business Manager, International
Brotherhood of Electrical Workers Local 300 (retired)

Nuclear is now gaining recognition as not only desirable but necessary in the effort to provide needed energy for the world in an environmentally responsible manner. Meredith's book provides practical tools for nuclear advocates to ensure that our existing nuclear assets are preserved and that new nuclear power facilities are licensed. This book is a *must read* for anyone engaging with the public on nuclear power issues.

— Eugene S. Grecheck,
Past President, American Nuclear Society

So many would-be pro-nuclear advocates stop before they even start, daunted by the success of the anti-nuclear movement and overwhelmed by the seemingly endless negative press about nuclear energy. Meredith's book is the antidote to the "why bother?" mindset that has ossified the nuclear industry for decades. Her book demystifies the advocacy process with no-nonsense advice, practical strategies, and step-by-step instructions for building an advocacy practice and achieving success. And don't forget to share some brownies!

— Andrea Jennetta, Publisher, *Fuel Cycle Week*

Campaigning for Clean Air

STRATEGIES FOR PRO-NUCLEAR ADVOCACY

Campaigning for Clean Air

STRATEGIES FOR PRO-NUCLEAR ADVOCACY

Meredith Angwin

CARNOT
COMMUNICATIONS

Campaigning for Clean Air: Strategies for Pro-Nuclear Advocacy

Dedicated to George Angwin.
Marrying you was the best decision of my life.

TABLE OF CONTENTS

AUTHOR'S INTRODUCTION

I NEVER MEANT TO BE AN ADVOCATE. I was always somewhat torn between being a chemist (my vocation) and writing (more than an avocation). "Advocacy" and "organizing" were not words in my vocabulary, or at least, not words I would have used about my own activities. So how did this change?

I will start with my decision to be a chemist. I was always interested in science, and I decided to major in chemistry. I figured a chemist could work hard and make some incremental progress that would help the world. I was a good student, but not brilliant. I figured chemists just had to be good, not spectacular. (Unlike physics majors, who seemed to be all about "Theory of Everything or Bust!") Chemists could be merely competent: giant breakthroughs are not required in chemistry. If I were going to school today, I would major in engineering. But back then, I didn't think of that.

In many ways, this "incremental progress" idea was a good grounding for a later-life career in advocacy. I constantly think of so many ways to "move the needle" to increase acceptance of nuclear energy. But just as I thought of my career in chemistry, I only want to help make some progress. Nuclear energy is the *Power to Save the World,* as in the title of Gwyneth Craven's ground-breaking book. However, as an activist, I know I won't personally be able to Save the World. I can contribute to a better world, and that is enough.

So, perhaps the next question is: why nuclear energy? That question has an easy answer, but perhaps a long one. I began my career in the 70s with an interest in energy. Like every other right-thinking person, I was interested in renewable energy. I had worked toward a Ph.D. (which I did not complete) in mineral chemistry, and so I gravitated toward geothermal energy.

I became one of the first women project managers at the Electric Power Research Institute. I was a project manager in geothermal energy, in charge of projects that aimed to increase the efficiency and use of geothermal power. So, how could life get better? I was in the Renewable Resources group at the primary research arm of electric utilities in this country. It was all good!

Except when it wasn't. I became aware that an all-renewable future just would not work.

We were a very sincere group of people in the Renewable Resources group at EPRI, and we did our best to site projects in places where they would be successful. To my shock, I found that our wonderful renewable projects were often fought, tooth and nail, by intervenors like the Sierra Club. How can they do that?

But a worse shock was how little power these projects produced. They were so small! And most of them were what we now call "intermittent." The solar projects worked (and still work) when the sun was shining. The wind projects were (in my opinion) a disaster of inefficiency. Although I still kept my "incremental progress" idea, it became clear to me that the problems of renewables were beyond "incremental progress" to solve. An all-renewable grid was just not possible.

Although solar panels and wind turbines have improved tremendously since those days, the diffuse-energy nature of renewable resources still means that an all-renewable grid is not possible. Renewable power cannot support a modern civilization with warm, well-lit living spaces, easy transportation, and clean, efficient hospitals.

I had worked on cleaning up fossil fuels (another story; I'm proud of my patents in this field), but I became drawn more toward nuclear power. Nuclear was steady (as fossil can be), but it didn't put junk and acid gases up into the air. I was very happy when I was able to join the nuclear group at EPRI. In that group, I was indeed making "incremental progress" in an area where such progress could work to make a better world.

Finally, I was where I wanted to be, and progress was being made! After I left EPRI, I started a small consulting company. Many of our clients were nuclear power plants.

Much later, when my husband and I moved to Vermont, for our semi-retirement and to be nearer our grandchildren, I went back to my avocation of writing.

After my career in renewables and nuclear, I wanted to do something to encourage nuclear power. I decided to write a novel, with nuclear power as the background. The novel was a mystery, which took place in and around a nuclear plant.

The plant wouldn't melt down or be in any danger of hurting anyone, and the background would be day-to-day life at the plant. People would absorb some information about nuclear power by reading the book. Meanwhile, in the book, one man would be murdered, rather spectacularly, and suspects would abound.

It was a good idea, and I think *Nuclear Gentleman* is a good book. It is not yet published.

There was one problem with the book. I needed more information to make the background truly solid. I had worked on water chemistry and materials research. I had visited several nuclear plants. *But*—I had never actually worked at a nuclear plant. I needed someone to review the novel: someone who was knowledgeable about daily life at nuclear plants.

Meanwhile, I had kept my eyes out for pro-nuclear letters to the editor and for local courses on energy issues. I met local pro-nuclear people and began emailing with them and talking with them: Dr. Robert Hargraves and Howard Shaffer. I took Hargraves' class on "Rethinking Nuclear Power" and met some more pro-nuclear people. That was great.

Shaffer had been in the submarine service and worked at several nuclear power plants. He wrote a pro-nuclear letter in the local paper, and I contacted him. He was the perfect reviewer! I asked him to review my book. He did. However, a favor of that size requires a reciprocal favor. Shaffer asked me to come to a hearing about Vermont Yankee. He often went to such hearings, and I went with him.

I went to the hearing. Oh my. Street theater. An anti-nuclear state representative pulling the microphone away from the hearing moderator, grappling with him for it. A man dressed in a gorilla suit labelled "NRC." Anti-nuclear people shouting whenever pro-nuclear people spoke. Amazing things.

I was a person of rather academic pursuits, like water chemistry research. I had never seen anything like this circus that called itself a "hearing."

After that meeting, I didn't think of becoming an "activist," but I did begin noticing anti-nuclear letters in the local press. I began writing some of my own letters to the editor. Then I began following some pro-nuclear blogs, because they had good information on current nuclear controversies. (I had nuclear information but it wasn't useful because it wasn't about the controversies. The number of people who would care about my expertise in managing all-volatile-water-chemistry in secondary-side water in PWRs was—a pretty small number.)

I think the real turning point for me was when I was going to attend (just attend) a pro- and anti-nuclear debate. But the moderator was a bit naive: he was shocked that the plant would not send anyone to take the pro-nuclear side. (I write about this debate in chapter 21.) A friend of the moderator called me: would I represent the pro-nuclear side? He had seen my letters in the newspapers.

This was a small debate in a local library. "Sure," I said. "I'll do it." How hard could it be? I knew my subject, I knew the usual anti-nuclear accusations and how to counter them. Really, how hard could it be? (When I got to the Tracy Memorial Library, I learned reporters would be covering the debate. Good thing I didn't know that at first.)

I did all right. Howard helped me prepare, and I am deeply grateful! I also decided to use some images that I knew the opponents would use, and I explained those images instead of dodging them. This worked pretty well: it's always better to explain something than to just say it is "misleading."

I had some good ideas, but I definitely wished I had more of a road map. The man I was debating knew more than his anti-nuclear phrases: he knew how to be an advocate for his cause. He wasn't all that technically knowledgeable, but he knew how to debate. He had his ducks in order. He had had training.

It was hard.

Since then, I learned a lot of advocacy and have done a lot of advocacy. I think that with my pro-nuclear friends, we have moved the needle toward wider acceptance of nuclear power. For example, I'm pretty okay with debates now. I am especially proud of a book that my husband and I published, *Voices for Vermont Yankee,* with pro-nuclear statements from many people.[1] (These were statements people made at a hearing of the Vermont Public Service Board.) I am pleased that Howard Shaffer and I received Presidential Citations from the American Nuclear Society president, for our educational and outreach work.

I am happy to be an advocate for clean, safe, abundant nuclear energy.

I am also happy to be involved in our region's major energy issues: I am a member of the Coordinating Committee of the Consumer Liaison Group of ISO-NE (the grid operator). I have learned a lot in the years since that first debate.

A year ago, I decided that I would write the book I wish I had had, that day at Tracy Memorial Library. I would write a book on how to be a pro-nuclear advocate.

This is the book.

CHAPTER ONE

A DAY IN THE LIFE

(of Three Nuclear Supporters)

*(Please note that the three people in this chapter
are fictional characters.)*

Joseph Hayes

MARCH IS FAMOUS FOR CHANGEABLE WEATHER, and early March has dreadful weather in the Northeast. At least, plant manager Joseph Hayes finds the weather depressing: gray skies, a dreary fall of rain mixed with sleet, and piles of dirty snow. No sunshine, but not weather bad enough to deter the protestors who will show up to protest the plant's operations the next day. "Six years since Fukushima, and this killer plant is still operating."

Every March 11 has been a security nightmare since the tsunami wiped out 20,000 lives in Japan and caused three reactors to melt down. Radiation cost no lives, at the plant or elsewhere, but the meltdown is what people remember. Mostly because of the protestors. They chain themselves to the gates. They bring giant puppets. They bring a few people from Japan to stir the guilt of Americans. Americans dropped the bombs on Japan. Americans designed the power plants that melted down. How much Japan has suffered due to the Americans and their love of nuclear fission!

The protestors give interviews to the press, emotional outpourings of fear and shame and "yes, it hasn't happened here yet, but it will." Sometimes the press asks Joseph or his press liaison Ellen Beatty for an interview, too. Everything Joseph or Ellen says is true: Nobody died from radiation in Japan, the latest reports show that no uptick in cancer can be expected, the plant was hit by one of the largest tsunamis in world history, and this American plant is on a river, not a place for tsunamis. His plant has high safety ratings from the Nuclear Regulatory Commission, emits no greenhouse gases, produces dependable power in cold weather and snowstorms. His plant was reliable while gas-fired plants were going off-line without gas availability, and coal plants went off-line as the coal piles froze.

When the newspaper articles come out, sometimes the reporters give him a line or two. Whatever he says always comes out sounding apologetic: "Plant spokesmen deny . . ."

"Plant spokesmen deny"? Someday, he would like to see a story including the words "Scaremongers attempt to terrify about nuclear accidents that they claim *could* happen here." Well, that sentence will never be written. Meanwhile, there's no reason to like early March.

Jennifer Barkley

A FEW WEEKS AGO she allowed it to slip: her husband was a Navy Nuke when they were married (he works for an architectural/engineering firm now, building all sorts of bridges and power plants). She is in favor of nuclear energy.

It was like coming out of the closet . . . in the old days. Back then, when a person "admitted" he was gay, he could expect plenty of scorn in return. That sort of "coming out" is what she has experienced.

It has not been fun. The wives of nuclear plant workers have each other for support, but she feels very alone now. She is a member of the board of the art museum; they don't expect nuclear supporters there. Two board members were very direct in pointing out that they were also active (or even board members) in anti-nuclear organizations such as the Sierra Club and Beyond Nuclear. They didn't just say this: they made it very clear that they held the moral high ground by boasting of their anti-nuclear involvement.

One of the women from the art museum was also in her yoga class, and she began arguing with Jennifer after class. Jennifer tried her hardest to duck, but the woman was so sure that "nuclear is evil" that she just kept right on going, attracting a crowd. Some of the other yogis moved away quickly, embarrassed by the conflict right after savasana in class. It wasn't appropriate. You were supposed to leave class in a calm and relaxed state, open to the world and free of "maya," the unreality of materialistic desires. Having a fight about electricity supplies broke the spirit of calmness.

Some women had walked away from the confrontational group. Jennifer wondered whether some of these women actually supported nuclear energy but didn't want to admit it. The people who stayed in the little group attacking her and nuclear . . . they certainly opposed nuclear power and were quite happy to admit it.

She remembers reading an interview with Gwyneth Cravens, author of *Power to Save the World: The Truth About Nuclear Energy*. Cravens, a serious yogi, hid the subject of her book from her yoga friends until the book was about to be published. At that point, there was no hiding the topic. When she revealed its actual contents and the explanations about why nuclear power was cleaner and safer than all the other options, Cravens found the group more accepting than she had expected. In her own yoga class, Jennifer is finding less acceptance.

What is wrong here? Her husband is successful, she doesn't have to work, she spends her time on boards of interest to her (the art museum), at yoga, and painting. She has an "art name" and frequently sells her work at street fairs, where people look for her and are eager to buy her watercolors. And yet, just like that, she finds herself under attack about nuclear energy. Her position does not save her from scorn.

Coming out of the closet isn't fun.

Mary Freeman

IT WAS EASY TO MAKE THE DECISION to take their daughter, Grace, out of gymnastics. Two other girls had told her daughter that her dad, her wonderful dad, killed people with radiation by working at the nuclear plant. Grace came home in tears.

Mary gave Grace a pep talk, of course, and explained that her father helped people and did not hurt them. She reminded Grace that her father was in the volunteer fire department, in order to help people. Grace listened, and even talked about joining the fire department when she was older, because girls could join, right? The incident seemed to have been resolved.

But Grace came home from the next gymnastics lesson once again in tears. This time, the girls who had confronted her earlier had recruited more girls to their side. They told Grace that the plant should shut down because it caused cancer, and her father was a bad man. Mary knew the children were just copying their parents' ideas, but she couldn't have Grace coming back in tears all the time.

After this incident, Mary went to the instructor and told the woman that her daughter was being bullied in the gymnastics class, and her daughter no longer trusted some of the girls when they had to take turns "spotting" each other for safety.

The teacher said that this was unfortunate, but she wasn't at all sure what she could do. Most of the parents were anti-nuclear, and they would support their children's actions. The parents would say that Grace needed to be ready to face the facts of what her father's work entailed. The teacher was not going to step into the middle of the nuclear controversy. She would talk to the class about being polite, but she didn't think her talk would do much good.

Mary was sure that whatever the teacher said wouldn't "do much good" because the teacher was going to be so restrained in what she said, for fear of offending the parents. Mary knew that the teacher's assessment was realistic. But Mary's conversation still left Grace in a miserable situation in the gymnastics class.

There was only one after-school gymnastics program in the town. But twenty miles away, in a bigger town, there were two such programs. Mary planned to investigate the programs, though driving would be a pain. Instead of being able to bike or walk to gymnastics, Grace would have to be driven three times a week, and Mary would be chauffeur.

Mary wondered whether she should hang out exclusively with the families of plant employees and people known to support the plant. Maybe there were afterschool programs that mostly attracted plant supporters? Mary realized that that was actually an odd idea.

However, the fact was that Grace loved gymnastics. So a bit of commuting would have to be okay.

Looking forward

JOSEPH, JENNIFER, AND MARY are fictional characters. To build them, I took a little bit of this person's story and a little bit of that person's story. But the stories, and the emotions, are true.

All these people support the only type of electricity source that can provide abundant clean energy for the future. And yet they all feel very alone.

This book is about supporting nuclear power but not being alone while you support it. It is about knowing your facts and finding your community. It's about being pro-nuclear and having fun doing it.

Joseph, Jennifer, and Mary have similar problems. They each feel alone and isolated. By working together, by emerging from their separation, they can join a community and support our best hope for a clean, safe energy future.

CHAPTER TWO

WHY SUPPORT NUCLEAR

THIS CHAPTER IS ABOUT WHY to support nuclear energy. It is worth your time to support nuclear energy and its necessary infrastructure. This chapter will attempt to explain why you should do so.

If you are reading this book, I can make the moderate assumption that you are in favor of nuclear energy, at least to some extent. This chapter is about why to publicly *support* nuclear power. Hopefully, you already understand many of the *advantages* of nuclear power compared to fossil and renewable energy. My book contains five short "white paper" documents on why I support nuclear power. You can also find excellent information on nuclear power in *Power to Save the World* by Gwyneth Cravens,[2] *Terrestrial Energy* by William Tucker,[3] and the eBook *Greenjacked!* by Geoff Russell.[4]

This chapter is not about nuclear power *per se.* Instead, it describes why it is worth your time to work in favor of your favorite nuclear facility. It is about why it is important to actively support continued operation of your local nuclear plant or nuclear research facility or fuel fabrication factory.

Here are the three main reasons to be an active supporter.

1) *Show up to help others show up*

There are many groups organized to protest about and attempt to stop nuclear energy from being used. These groups are old, well organized, and well funded. They often have leaders who have taken masters degrees or one-year courses in "activism organization." (Yes, I was also surprised such things exist.) These groups are very effective in taking over the public discourse. Soon, it appears that everybody hates nuclear energy. At that point, anyone who likes it is afraid to say so.

When you show up to defend nuclear energy, it encourages others to realize they are not alone.

When you visibly support nuclear energy, it makes it more acceptable for others to be pro-nuclear.

2) *Show up to have others hear your views*

You aren't going to convince the dedicated anti-nuclear people. Oh, we are all happy when occasionally a nuclear opponent changes his mind. But that is not the goal.

However, others will hear you. Reporters will report what you say. Eventually, instead of "environmental groups protested the power plant," the news reports will read "supporters and opponents of the power plant spoke at the hearing yesterday."

And then, eventually, the positive messages get heard. Reporters like to report a good "he said, she said," and industry spokesmen can rarely give them a decent sound bite. A knowledgeable nuclear supporter can get quoted, and someone reading the paper may have his or her views changed, if only a little.

For people to hear about pro-nuclear views, pro-nuclear people have to show up.

3) *Show up to increase civility*

In some public meetings I have attended, nuclear supporters were bullied and even physically intimidated.

This only happens when the nuclear opponents outnumber nuclear supporters by about two to one. When the numbers are more even, the meeting is more civil. Many meetings are like a grammar school playground. For increased civility, supporters need to be there.

Californians for Green Nuclear Power t-shirt: Diablo Canyon and green.
Credit: Rod Adams

And, frankly, be visible. I suggest having some sort of insignia that makes you visible (green t-shirts have been used in California, large pro-nuclear buttons have been used in Vermont). Bullying techniques don't work as well when there are two good-sized groups of people in a meeting. More about this in the chapters on meetings.

The only defense against lies, fear-mongering, and street theater is truth, honesty, and being there.

Do it.

ACTION ITEM:

Get on a list. Contact your local facility and ask if they keep an email list to keep interested persons informed about upcoming hearings that concern the plant. (They probably do.) Ask to be on it. To do this, you will ask for the plant's "public relations" or "public outreach" person.

CHAPTER THREE

THE NUCLEAR COMMUNITY

To HAVE A COMMUNITY, you first have to find that community. Unlike a religious community (just join the one of your choice) or a political community (become active in the party of your choice), the nuclear community is comparatively hard to find. There is no big organization set up to be pro-nuclear.

I will now ask hearty forgiveness from the American Nuclear Society,[5] of which I am a member, and Nuclear Matters.[6] The ANS is a professional society. To join it, you must have career background or education related to nuclear science or engineering. Joining Nuclear Matters is like joining the National Geographic Society: there are no local meetings. There are other national groups too, not as well known, but they also do not have local meetings.

If you are lucky, there may be some pro-nuclear groups near you.

For example, Northern California has many pro-nuclear groups. The Breakthrough Institute[7] is located in Oakland. It is an energy think tank that addresses worldwide issues and values nuclear power. It was founded in 2003 by Ted Nordhaus and Michael Shellenberger.

A local group, Californians for Green Nuclear Power (CGNP),[8] has been active for several years. Their main focus is to support the continued operation of Diablo Canyon. Dr. Gene Nelson and William Gloege are the principal founders.

The Thorium Energy Alliance (TEA)[9] supports the development of new reactors based on a thorium fuel cycle. TEA includes a group called Thorium Energy Silicon Valley. Dr. Alex Cannara and Dr. Bob Greene are co-directors. The Silicon Valley group has been active in supporting existing reactors on a state and national level, as well as in supporting new reactor development. Silicon Valley group members give talks at meetings and conferences, and some are regular commuters to energy hearings in Sacramento.

Recently, two more groups have been formed. The noted environmentalist Michael Shellenberger of Breakthrough Institute founded a new international group, Environmental Progress.[10] Two mothers, Kristin Zaitz and Heather Matteson, started Mothers for Nuclear.[11] These groups are now active in several states. I suggest you look at their websites and join them.

In short, looking at California pro-nuclear groups, I see a vibrant and ever-changing landscape of nuclear supporters. Which means, of course, that I have undoubtedly left people and groups out of my listing. I am not aiming for completeness in this short book. But I will take a moment to ask for forgiveness from all the people in California I have not mentioned.

The more the merrier

IT IS WONDERFUL THAT California has so many varied pro-nuclear groups. I believe that when a message is supported by many groups, the message is more credible.

In practical terms, when many pro-nuclear groups cosponsor a meeting, reporters and the public get a very solid impression about nuclear advocacy. All the groups will have different "takes" on advocacy: different leaders, different strengths, and different strategies. It's all good! Or to say the same thing in a more old-fashioned way: When it comes to advocacy—the more the merrier!

However, for the rest of this chapter, I am assuming you are starting from scratch with no local groups near you.

How will you find your pro-nuclear community?

Be pro-nuclear and visible

MY FIRST LESSON IN FINDING community is that you need to be visibly pro-nuclear, so they can find you!

Much of this book is about being visible in various ways: online and in person. For example: sending letters to the editor, having a blog, speaking at meetings. At one point, I predicted that anti-nuclear groups would bring brochures and newsletters and put them on tables outside the hall at my town meeting. I put some pro-nuclear information (copied at the local copy shop) on the same table and stood near it. Quite a few people said that they were so glad I was there; they had never seen someone being at the town meeting and being pro-nuclear. Two women hugged me!

It was a revelation to me that so many people were in favor of nuclear power. Since then, I have learned that polls show that two-thirds of people are in favor of using nuclear power and even expanding it, but slightly less than one-third of them think that a majority in their community favored nuclear energy. This is illustrated in 2016 polling data by Bisconti Research, Inc.

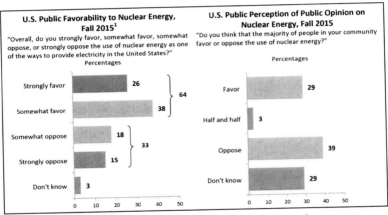

Bisconti Research survey: two-thirds of Americans favor nuclear energy, but they think that only one-third of Americans favor it.
Credit: Bisconti Research, with link http://www.bisconti.com/index.html

Distributing flyers at a town meeting may not be for you. That's me, and sometimes I wonder about myself. There are many other ways to be visible.

Throughout the year the Nuclear Regulatory Commission or your local plant may hold various public meetings you can attend.

Most of the time, plant officials or public supporters will speak at these meetings, and you can introduce yourself to them afterwards, privately. Or you can look for people who self-identify as nuclear supporters: people wearing clothing with the company logo, people with the twin dolphin pin of the Silent Service pinned to their lapels. Speak up and introduce yourself! You may be surprised by how many other local nuclear supporters you can meet, and there will be even more supporters to whom they can introduce you.

Pro-nuclear people are a majority who think they are a minority.

Collect names if you can

NOBODY HAS TO GIVE YOU their name, but if they come up to you at a public place and express their pro-nuclear feelings, for Pete's sake, have a sign-up sheet where they can write their name and their email address. Also, if you possibly can, look over what they wrote. Some people have terrible handwriting, and (voice of experience here) you don't want to come back with twenty lovely names and discover that you can't read seven of the email addresses, or the addresses bounce. Don't beat yourself up if this happens: we aren't always in a position to do a good "legibility review." Try to be sure everything is legible. If people are willing to write on a tablet, the problem is solved. But electronic devices can be intimidating. If you give a pro-nuclear talk, even if only five people attend, collect the names on a sign-up sheet. Be sure that you say, "Please share your name if you are willing to be on our mailing list and keep up with this subject. I send very few emails: you will not be spammed."

Also, when you write letters to the editor or appear on TV or radio (more about that later), people may contact you. Be open. Talk to people. Meet them for coffee if you can.

Is there a pro-nuclear letter to the editor in your paper? Look up the person who wrote it, call her, and tell her about what you are doing. Would she be willing to be on your email list?

Is there a veterans organization near you? Can you ask to speak to it? Can you ask someone in the organization to send an email note to its members, asking them to contact you if they were in the nuclear navy, or if they are pro-nuclear energy?

If you are near a plant or a national lab, don't forget them. See if you can speak at the facility. See if you can hold a meeting nearby, and announce it in their internal e-newsletter.

Several chapters later in this book are devoted to social media. The good news about social media is that it is inexpensive to use (both in time and money), and many people follow Facebook, Twitter, and LinkedIn, etc. The bad news is that it is international in scope, which is not that helpful to a local activist. However, you can join some pro-nuclear groups or pages, set up your own page, and then invite people to "like" your page or join your group, or whatever. Be sure your page is devoted to the plant or facility that you want to support: it is the best way to get at least a reasonable portion of people who will be active on your behalf.

Social media will give you many wonderful links, but often hide the email addresses (this is true of all social media). You can only reach these people by using the social media portal. That can be good enough. They may well answer your call to action, write letters to the editors, and so forth. But you will end up with multiple lists. You might ask them, however, for their email addresses. Try to get as many people as possible on an email list. That is the most useful kind of list.

Collect local names

SO FAR, WE HAVE BEEN discussing pro-nuclear websites, Twitter streams, and Facebook pages and groups. This is not enough. All politics is local, and you should also be joining local groups of various types. Political groups may have many supporters, but they may also put you in a box of "being Republican" or "being a Democrat." This can limit your appeal to the other side of the political fence. On the other hand, you will find many active and interested people in these groups.

But there are other groups also . . . nature-loving groups that don't want to see habitat destroyed with wind turbines. There are many pro-nuclear environmentalists. You can assure them that they are not alone.

But basically, be visible and ask for names with *any* group. Follow your own interests (little theater, music, etc.). There are pro-nuclear people in every group, and most of these people think they are alone and everyone disagrees with them about nuclear energy. By being pro-nuclear and visible, you will attract notice (and capture names) wherever you are.

Grow your list, in your locality.

ACTION ITEM:

Start a list. You don't have to go anywhere to start it. Just write down the names and email addresses of people you know are pro-nuclear. Make the email addresses into a "group" on your email program: "Pro-nuclear group."

Later, this list will grow.

ABOUT THE
WHITE PAPERS

THERE ARE MANY EXCELLENT books on *why* to support nuclear power: this book is about *how* to support it. As I finished the book, however, I began to realize that it was missing something. In most chapters, I don't talk much about why I personally support nuclear power.

There was a reason for that. When I was writing the book, I didn't want to duplicate the excellent and extensive literature in favor of nuclear power. Unfortunately, by not duplicating, I left something important out of the book. I left out my own reasons for supporting nuclear energy.

The five short "White Paper" chapters describe some of the reasons I advocate for expanded use of nuclear power. The chapters are not meant to be complete or all-inclusive. I decided to place them throughout the book rather than have them one after another, which would interrupt the flow of the main book.

I call these chapters "white papers," though they are more like "my thoughts" or maybe even "talking points." The chapters are:

Nuclear Power for Clean Air

Nuclear Energy Safety

The Big Accidents

Nuclear Energy for Efficient Land Use

Nuclear Energy Around the World

WHITE PAPER 1

NUCLEAR POWER FOR CLEAN AIR

CLEAN AIR IS THE MAIN REASON I support nuclear power. I chose to name this book *Campaigning for Clean Air*. My early career included much research on how to clean up the air from fossil and even geothermal technologies.

As I noted in my introduction, I started my career in geothermal power. I spent a fair amount of time evaluating hydrogen sulfide clean-up methods for geothermal energy. Hydrogen sulfide is the gas that smells like rotten eggs. Gas wells often bring up considerable amounts of hydrogen sulfide, and so do some geothermal wells. Some well water also smells of hydrogen sulfide; in general, this is just a nuisance. In the oil and gas industry, however, the gas is not just a nuisance: it can be fatal. The gas is very toxic, and people working in oil fields have died due to uncontrolled releases. Evaluating methods for cleaning up hydrogen sulfide was my first introduction to air pollution.

But then I moved on to a job where I was doing research in cleaning air pollution from fossil fuels. I was working on nitrogen oxide (NOx) reduction methods, and I have two patents in this area. NOx is a mixture of two forms of nitrogen oxides: it is responsible for the brown color of photochemical smog and, even worse, is part of the cause of acid rain. Later, I worked on dry scrubbing for sulfur oxides, which also contribute to acid rain.

Nuclear power emits no hydrogen sulfide, no greenhouse gases, no acid gases (such as NOx and sulfur oxides or SOx), no dust, no smoke, and no mercury. Clean air is a major reason why I support nuclear.

Note: Nuclear plants do release a small amount of radiation to their surroundings. This subject is covered in the second white paper, which is about safety.

Dirty air from fossil: acid gases and particulate

I HATE NOx. The problem with nitrogen oxides is that you can't get away from it. NOx is produced when air burns itself: the nitrogen in the air combines with the oxygen in the air, in a very hot flame. You can't get rid of NOx by using a cleaner fuel. The air is always there, and at high temperature, the air burns itself.

The laws of thermodynamics show that you get a higher efficiency from an engine—you get more kilowatt hours (kWh) per pound of fuel—if you burn the fuel at a higher temperature. But when you burn at higher temperatures, the air burns itself and makes NOx. That's why I hate NOx. It's built into efficient combustion processes in such a deep way. NOx is not merely *hard* to avoid. If you want an efficient engine based on combustion, NOx is *impossible* to avoid.

SOx is another acid gas: sulfur oxides that arise from fuels containing sulfur. Governments in Europe and North America are requiring ever-stricter limits on the sulfur content of diesel fuels, for example.

Both of the acid gases, NOx and SOx, are combustion products that cause pollution. (You can scrub the fuel of sulfur and reduce SOx. Not so easy with NOx.) NOx can be partially controlled by adding ammonia to the outgas stream, usually along with catalysts.

It's not easy to estimate how much NOx and SOx are emitted by power plants. To estimate acid gases from a power plant, you need to know the fuel, the combustion temperature, and the type of pollution control the plant uses. In contrast, it is easy to estimate the amount of carbon dioxide produced in fossil-burning plants. The carbon dioxide emissions depend pretty directly on the type of fuel that is burned, not on combustion temperature, pollution control methods, and so forth.

According to the Nuclear Energy Institute, in 2014 America's ninety-nine nuclear reactors prevented 960,000 short tons of sulfur dioxide and 480,000 short tons of nitric oxide emissions.[12] Looking at the estimates over the years, this seems reasonable.

I think we don't know exactly how much acid gas emissions are prevented by using nuclear plants instead of fossil. Still . . . there's a big difference between "none" (nuclear plants) and "up to 960,000 short tons of sulfur dioxide (mostly coal plants)."

According to James Hansen, a pioneer in climate change science and awareness, nuclear power may have saved 1.8 million lives that would have ended if fossil fuels had been used in place of nuclear power. This is due to the clean air benefits of nuclear power, compared to emissions from fossil fuel sources.[13]

Another fossil pollutant is particulate. Particulate matter is the term for particles found in the air, like dust, dirt, soot, smoke, and liquid droplets. Particulate can be inhaled into and accumulate in the respiratory system. Small particulates (less than 2.5 micrometers in diameter) have major health risks because the particles are so small that they can lodge deeply into the lungs. Once again, the amount of particulate emitted depends on the type of pollution control in use at the coal or biomass plant. So it is hard to quantify.[14]

Yes, this is all hard to quantify. Moving away from the air a little, we can look at the fate of one particulate: coal ash. Coal ash is toxic, and it is frequently stored in lagoons (lined or unlined), and the runoff or pond breaches can cause environmental damage to rivers. Unfortunately, it is hard to get a handle on this. One advocacy website includes information,[15] but the EPA website with real data is no longer maintained.[16] The new EPA website is hard to follow.

Two years ago, the EPA passed the first-ever rule for regulating coal ash disposal. The rule regulates coal ash as a "solid waste" but not as a "hazardous waste." Also, the rule is "self-regulating"; this means that the federal government does not enforce it. However, utilities can face legal actions (by citizens and states) if they don't comply with the EPA rule.

As you can probably guess, with enforcement by lawsuit, coal ash regulation is a confusing state-by-state situation. In my opinion, the coal ash ponds are probably going to be there for a long time.[17]

To summarize, fossil fuel burning puts many pollutants into the environment, particularly into the air we breathe. Nuclear power doesn't. Nuclear for Clean Air!

(Wouldn't it be nice if all energy producers were required to document and report all of their waste products? Wouldn't it be nice if fossil reporting requirements were the same as nuclear?)

For further reading on nuclear power's contribution to a clean environment, I also recommend Gwyneth Cravens' *Power to Save the World*, and the websites of the American Nuclear Society and Nuclear Energy Institute.

Greenhouse gases from fossil fuels

THE GOOD NEWS ABOUT greenhouse gases (carbon dioxide) from combustion processes is that it is *very* easy to estimate. Just look at the fuel: almost every bit of the carbon in the fuel turns into carbon dioxide.

The bad news is that many people who support nuclear don't think man-made climate change is an issue. These supporters get annoyed when there is too much emphasis on how nuclear energy prevents carbon dioxide emissions.

Well, I think greenhouse gases and man-made climate change are issues. And I am writing a *personal* essay about why I support nuclear. Still, there are many reasons to support nuclear energy. If preventing greenhouse gases is not one of your reasons, just skip reading this section.

Unlike combustion, nuclear energy does not emit carbon dioxide at the power plant. Even most nuclear opponents admit this. However, nuclear opponents claim that the "lifecycle" emissions from nuclear energy make it just as bad as any other energy source in terms of greenhouse gases. Lifecycle emissions include emissions from building the plants, mining fuel, transporting fuel, as well as emissions from plant operation. So I will compare lifecycle emissions.

The Intergovernmental Panel on Climate Change (IPCC) has done extensive research on lifecycle greenhouse gas emissions from various technologies. For a power source, lifecycle emissions studies include the emissions from mining, manufacturing, shipping, and everything else . . . not just the emissions while the plant is making power. IPCC does these studies every few years, and this is a personal essay, not a research paper. So I will mostly refer to the Wikipedia article that has summaries of many IPCC studies,[18] and studies by other groups as well.

The 2014 IPCC study used hundreds of scientific papers to estimate lifecycle emissions of greenhouse gases from various technologies. I list the median values (from many papers) of grams of carbon dioxide per kWh from that IPCC study:

- Coal: 820 grams/kWh
- Gas combined cycle: 490
- Rooftop solar photovoltaic (PV): 41
- Nuclear: 12
- Wind onshore: 11
- Wind offshore: 12

This IPCC study shows the big picture, including many studies and worldwide data. Instead of looking at this type of report by intergovernmental panels, I can look a little closer to home.

When Vermont Yankee shut down, the power it produced was replaced by gas-fired plants. The New England grid used about five percent more gas-fired power in the year after Vermont Yankee closed. The nuclear power was replaced, pretty much kWh for kWh, by electricity from natural gas. The loss of Vermont Yankee led to three million more metric tons of carbon dioxide being produced by New England's energy sector—except that coal-fired generators were also used less, so the total carbon dioxide emissions only increased by two million metric tons, year to year. In other words, New England shut down a nuclear plant, and even though we used less coal, our greenhouse gas emissions increased.[19]

A side note about greenhouse gases and nuclear energy

Many nuclear opponents will not use the results of IPCC (United Nations) or EIA (US Energy Information Administration) studies for lifecycle studies. Instead, opponents find their own favorite studies, which supposedly show that nuclear energy has high lifecycle greenhouse gas emissions.

For example, one such study claims that nuclear lifecycle emissions are twenty-five times the lifecycle emissions from wind turbines. In contrast, the average of IPCC-reviewed studies (averages listed above) showed nuclear and wind as having similar lifecycle greenhouse gas emissions.

Where did this twenty-five-times-wind number come from? Amazingly enough, in the twenty-five-times study, the researcher added something bizarre to his accounting of emissions ascribed to nuclear energy. He added "emissions from the burning of cities resulting from nuclear weapons explosions potentially resulting from nuclear energy expansion."

You can see the whole quote and an excellent critique of the complex roots of this "study" in this post by Charles Barton: "Does Nuclear Energy Really Equate to Nuclear War?"[20]

As a general rule, IPCC studies, or the "median" numbers (from many studies) in Wikipedia, are far better guides to lifecycle emissions than individual studies cleverly designed by nuclear opponents.

Nuclear energy is clean, safe, and abundant. That is why I support it.

CHAPTER FOUR

BUILDING YOUR TEAM

CHAPTER 3 FEATURED MANY ways you can find nuclear supporters, and how to keep track of them when you find them (get
their names and email addresses). This work yields something
important: a "list." Marketers and political campaigners spend
a great deal of energy on strategies for "growing your list."
This is important work, because your list partially defines your
reach and your influence.

However, a list is not a team.

You want at least some of the people on your list to be
willing to take action. For this, you have to build a team:
people who will take action and take initiative to support
nuclear energy.

How do you build your team? In some ways, it is easy:

- Meet for brownies and coffee
- Set near-term goals
- Have fun

In other ways, building your team is hard. Many of the list-building activities have a long geographical range. You will have list members within a quick drive of your home, and you will have list members on the other side of the world. You have two teams.

Both teams are important, but the nearby team is more important. The virtual team (the ones you can't meet very easily) can be a tremendous asset for organizing information, writing letters, donations and more. But this chapter will focus on the people you *can* meet, the team in your locality, the team that can carpool to a hearing, get together at someone's house to write letters, attend a public talk. The team you can touch is the important team.

The team you can touch

YOU MUST GET THE TEAM off on the right foot by *listening*. Nuclear supporters have their reasons for being supporters: ask them and listen to the answers. Think about what they said and how to incorporate it into the team activities. Ask them more questions on how to move their ideas into actions.

People who choose to work with a leader are buying into the leader. They are deciding that this person is honorable, and this person cares about me, and the two of us agree on a fair amount of stuff. My friend Guy Page, former newspaper owner and current communications director at Vermont Energy Partnership, explains that the way to get people's buy-in is simple: ask questions and listen to the answers.

The next step in team building is to have a goal that everyone is working towards. For your meetings with like-minded

Howard Shaffer, Dianne Amme, and Meredith Angwin at a rally for Vermont Yankee, October 2011.

people, you should be supporting a local nuclear plant or other nuclear facility. Local people, local projects. Having a local project will make it easy to come up with goals.

At the beginning, you yourself will choose the goals. Later, other members of the team choose other goals.

Tiny goals

ESPECIALLY AT THE BEGINNING, have small goals and celebrate when you succeed at the goals. For example, one team I know about had a goal of getting "some" letters into local papers. I would have encouraged a goal of something like "two letters into three local papers" because it is more measurable. At any rate, it is a small goal. After the letters appear, it is time to celebrate. Get together and congratulate the letter writers. If someone has a blog, reprint the letters on the blog. Praise the people who looked at the letters before they were sent.

Success breeds success.

Working toward goals

HERE ARE SOME EXAMPLES of near-term goals:

- A pro-nuclear letter writing campaign
- Attending a hearing
- Visiting a legislator and talking about nuclear energy

Unless there is an important hearing coming up, which goal you choose is not too important. What is important is getting together with people, having food with people (snacks or potlucks), and showing everyone that:

- They have supportive friends
- There are things they can do to support nuclear energy
- They can successfully accomplish some goals

Having fun (friends) and having accomplishments (doing things) are the two keystones of building a team. It's never easy, but we can learn from religious groups, political groups, and (gasp) our opponents.

Pro-nuclear groups tend to have what I call a Brownie Deficit. They don't get together often enough. When they get together, they tend to be very focused and a little bit afraid of saying the wrong thing.

In contrast, opponents get together, have potlucks, decide on costumes for their next street theater event, and so forth. Opponents often have a serious anti-nuclear social life. Pro-nuclear people, not so much.

You don't have to make nuclear advocacy your social life, but it's not a board meeting, either. At your meetings, have food on the table. Trade personal stories and nuclear ideas. Feel free to talk and to munch. Cure the Brownie Deficit.

Another way to start: Speakers

ONE OF THE EASIEST WAYS to get your group started is to have a speaker. Take the nearby people on your list, find a rentable room at a local museum, library, or house of worship. You can find a speaker from your local power plant or American Nuclear Society chapter, and kick off a meeting. Now, this is not outreach to the general public: this is building your team. This is not something you are going to advertise: this is team building.

In other words, this is invitation-only, which means you will probably have to pay rent for the room. (Groups that have open meetings, such as book discussion groups, can usually get free rooms at libraries.) But the rent won't be much, and you can ask people who attend to kick in a dollar or two.

One of the truths of the world is that people *like* to be included, as long as it is not too expensive. "We paid $40 to rent this room, so if you can, can you leave a donation of about two dollars?" This is transparency and also . . . this is the first opportunity for people to literally "buy in" to belonging to the group.

Be sure to have snacks, too!

Have something ready for people to take home after the meeting: at least a single sheet with the tentative (you can change it later) name of the group, and how to reach the organizers.

The second meeting: Making a difference

ASSUMING YOU STARTED with speakers, at the second meeting, you must accomplish something. The easiest thing is to write a few letters.

For a letter campaign you need three things:

- A subject or issue to write about
- Some stories, facts or data to support your comments
- A list of places to send the letters

It is best if one person chooses the issue and gives out a handout of facts about it. For almost any nuclear plant, you can start with a letter that describes how much carbon dioxide and nitrogen oxides would be produced if the same power were produced by a natural gas plant. You can then write letters about clean air. One letter might emphasize global warming, another one might focus on the role of acid gases (such as nitrogen oxides) in air pollution and acid rain. This is just an idea, but the point is that you don't have to know everything about everything to write a letter. You just have to do some research on something! Stories and facts that interest you will also be interesting to your readers.

The person who planned the letter is the "expert." Trust me, any member of your group can be this expert, with a little research. From what I have seen, anti-nuclear groups aren't particularly picky about their experts. Someone in your group who prepares and does research will be way ahead of most of the opponent "experts."

Another person in your group can be the media person: this person contacts local newspapers and websites, and puts together a local media list. You might be surprised how many local newspapers there are in an area. For example, some friends in California were concerned that they could never get a letter published in the *Los Angeles Times*. There is tremendous competition for space in the letters column in big newspapers. But it is easy to overlook the local papers. Local papers are carefully read, and it is much easier to get a letter in these papers. For example, the *San Luis Obispo Tribune* has a circulation of 35,000.

Here in Vermont, there are many local papers, including weeklies. These papers are often read very thoroughly. With electronic submissions, one letter can go to several papers.

Don't send everybody's letters all at once, but you may be pleasantly surprised at how easily your letters will be printed in local papers. (More about letter writing in another chapter.)

When the letters appear, the people who read the letters will be aware that there are pro-nuclear people in their areas. That's a win for your group. Celebrate it!

ACTION ITEM:

Make contact. Contact your local nuclear facility and see if they can provide your group with a speaker for a closed session of nuclear supporters.

BEFORE YOU GO PUBLIC: GETTING YOUR DUCKS IN ORDER

THE EARLIER PART OF this book was about finding your team. Now we have to look at what your team will do. The first thing is to get your ducks in order about your pro-nuclear information and your talking points.

Talking points are the points you want to make, along with the stories you want to tell and the facts that support these points. A good set of talking points is a valuable tool for any advocate. They can be used when talking to friends and neighbors, or they can serve as an instant back-up for letters to the editors.

Note: The White Paper sections of this book describe the advantages of nuclear energy. They may be a good starting point, but they are not a substitute for doing your own research and buying more comprehensive books about nuclear energy.

However, the chapters have many references and may help you design your talking points.

Realize your talking points won't be perfect

NO MATTER HOW CAREFULLY I prepare, once I am out in public, a nuclear opponent will quote some weird study from some weird website, and I will never have heard of it. I have come to realize that this is the fate of pro-nuclear people. We draw our information from a comparatively limited number of credible sources. The opponents draw their information from any source that agrees with them.

The opponents *will* throw something at you from left field. However, as Eisenhower said, "In preparing for battle I have always found that plans are useless, but planning is indispensable."[21]

Planning is important, and so are your talking points.

Kinds of talking points

THERE ARE TWO TYPES of talking points, general and specific. This first meeting is brainstorming, but as you fill in the talking points, you are going to have to know the difference between the different types of points in order to fill in your information. For each type of talking point, you need to know your allies, and where you can get information.

General issues

Many pro-nuclear points are applicable to most facilities. Nuclear as major source of low-carbon energy in the United

States, nuclear employment, etc. The White Paper chapters in this book are about general points.

Many anti-nuclear statements are also fairly general: What shall we do with the waste? Nuclear wouldn't exist without the Price-Anderson Act. Fukushima and Chernobyl will never be inhabited again. These statements will be applied to all nuclear facilities.

Specific issues

Pro-nuclear points can be *specific* to your area: stories about nuclear jobs, nuclear energy programs in local schools or colleges, national lab employment, local pride in nuclear, etc. This section depends on your local situation. If you are in coal country, nuclear clean air could be a good point with some and a bad point with others (people who depend on the coal industry).

Similarly, there can be anti-nuclear attacks that are specific to your facility. You must be ready to respond to them. West Coast plants will have to respond about earthquakes, mixed oxide fuel (MOX) facilities about plutonium, and national labs perhaps about weapons work. You have to know your own facility's situation. Actually, if you are reading this book, you probably already know the issues.

Work with someone on your first draft of talking points

SET UP A MEETING or phone call with a pro-nuclear friend (for me, it was usually Howard Shaffer) and promise to bring a list of pro-nuclear talking points to the meeting. Consider your lists, combine your lists, have coffee, talk about your latest family event, then get back to the talking points. Next to each point, make a list of background documents that support the point.

Beyond Google: If you have a talking point you want to use, but you don't know quite where to start to get good documents, you can reach out to a pro-nuclear blogger (they usually have contact information on the blog) or to the American Nuclear Society (ANS). The ANS can usually put you in touch with a local chapter.

The working draft

THERE ARE TWO SECOND DRAFTS: the inclusive draft and the working draft.

You should also have an all-inclusive draft . . . a major binder, a huge list of saved web articles, etc. Everything you can think of, for all types of issues. Keep this file and grow it, build it, expand it. It is important, but it is not your working draft. Include everything you think you might ever need to answer.

There are all sorts of software packages available for keeping track of large sets of files: Evernote has been recommended to me.[22]

Use special software, or just make a file on your computer. Start this process, and it will grow. But don't stress too much about it.

But you also need a much more limited working draft. The limited draft is the important draft for activism.

Your limited draft should include *three* well-articulated pro-nuclear statements, with backup information. It should also include a sheet of quick answers to some of the general questions and rebuttals to two or three of the local questions.

Why did I emphasize "three"? Because you can't do it all, but with three statements and backup, you have a start. Remember, no matter how well you get your facts together, there will be something outrageous said, something with no backup, and it will be asked as if it were a legitimate question. You cannot possibly be prepared for everything. But if you have a few statements that you can give as sound bites, a few statements that are clear and cogent rebuttals to the standard accusations in your locality, you will be well set.

In the second half of the book we'll discuss some of the public speaking tools you'll have in your activist's arsenal, like how to talk about (without talking too much about) the things you don't want to spend much time talking about.

Get help from those who know

WHEN YOU ARE PUTTING YOUR more general talking points together, you will be able to find excellent white papers at Nuclear Energy Institute, World Nuclear Association, American Nuclear Society, Breakthrough Institute, and Nuclear Matters. Professionals have been addressing these issues for years. For general pro-nuclear points and for rebuttals, these sources may be all you need.

You may also want to grow your library a bit. The nuclear opponents cradle Helen Caldicott's book under their arms: you can cradle Gwyneth Cravens' much better book, *Power* to *Save the World,* or William Tucker's *Terrestrial Energy.* Once you put your mind to it, obtaining information to rebut the nuclear opponents on general issues will be easy.

Help for specific issues

FOR SPECIFIC ISSUES, you may want some information from the facility itself. As a matter of fact, this is a good time to reach out to the outreach person at your facility.

Nuclear plants have at least one public relations or outreach person on staff. They can help you in many ways. They have access to their own press releases and websites that have answered many of the questions you need to have answered. They may have sponsored studies to show the economic value of their plants. They can even help you with materials on the general issues. If Nuclear Energy Institute (NEI) is reluctant to send two hundred copies of a white paper to some unknown person who claims she will give it to the local legislators, your outreach person at the local plant can probably help you get the copies you want.

Another important point is that the situation can be a collaboration between the supporters and the facility. This can be about talking points, and more. For example, they may know about hearings or events that are not yet in the newspapers. But they won't know about *you* unless you introduce yourself to them.

It is up to you if you are willing to take actual money from the facility. You will be called a "shill" whether or not you take it. However, you should have no issues about meeting with the facility outreach person and obtaining information and moral support for your work.

Have fun

YOU ARE GOING TO HAVE a wonderful row of ducks, and some great answers to most accusations. Later chapters on writing letters and on speaking in public will help you organize your ducks, and show your ducks to the world.

Have fun doing it, too. Most of the duck-in-order work includes getting together with other people. Hopefully you will meet people in person, but it can be online, too. Make the most of your meetings. Have coffee and brownies together. Enjoy that "we crazy outsiders stick together" feeling, so well expressed by Shakespeare: "We few, we happy few, we band of brothers."

And the band of brothers won at Agincourt, if you remember.

ACTION ITEM:

Start researching. Clip newspaper articles about your local facility. If one article describes a problem, review resources (NEI, Breakthrough Institute white papers) to understand the extent of the problem, which is probably exaggerated in the local press. (If it bleeds, it leads.)

CHAPTER SIX

EXPERT HELP

Unlike the nuclear opponents, who are willing to call people with no technical background as experts on radiation and plant operation, advocates need access to real experts. Where will we find them?

The facility itself

Let's start with your local power plant or facility. There are many ways for them to help you. Perhaps they have written white papers on the local issues. Their media room may have helpful press releases. Develop a relationship with their media outreach people: they may well be able to direct you to publicly available information that will aid you in stating the good news about the facility, and combatting the bad news.

Try and arrange for a tour of the plant or facility. An activist's credibility is increased by being able to say, "When I was there, I saw . . ." At the plant, managers are told about tours that are coming through. The managers will love to report to their staffs that pro-nuclear people are coming for a visit.

In many cases, people who work at a big company (including a power plant) cannot be quoted in the press about anything connected with the company. This is understandable: no company wants reporters interviewing random people at the company, and then accusing the company of "hiding things" or "being inconsistent" or whatever. Companies of all types control their outward-bound messages, whether the company is making electricity or laundry detergent. However, this company-wide decision can get in your way: when you want to speak to an expert, you know people at the plant have expertise . . . and they can't talk to you.

That is where you have to do the slow and steady work of getting to know the people in outreach. They can help.

However, they can't usually help you get the sort of thing you see in the press all the time: "Someone who did not wish to be identified explained that . . ."

Actually, you can't write that. The only reason people in the press can write about "people who don't wish to be identified" is that there is a long tradition that reporters do *not* have to reveal their sources. That is how reporters get around the gatekeepers. As an activist, your "sources" are not protected. As a matter of fact, I have never quite figured out whether bloggers are protected by this rule (I am a blogger), so I generally stay on the safe side of using quotations.

But . . . the gatekeepers (outreach people at the facility) can still help you find the information you need. Usually, this information is in public documents of various sorts. Remember, though, that working with you is not the outreach person's main job. If the plant is in the midst of a refueling outage, or there is a sudden raft of newspaper articles about the plant, the outreach people may not have much time for you. However, if you have built a relationship with them, it will be easier to get the information you need.

Getting specific-issue information

WELL, THIS IS ALL RATHER THEORETICAL. Let me give you an example. Vermont Yankee power plant leaked some tritium, which was detected in wells, on plant property, specifically designed to test water for any leaks. When the test wells detected tritium, there were many public comments that tritium was leaking into the groundwater and threatening everybody's health. This was not the case: it was only detected within the plant boundaries, at special test wells. But the fear-inducing comments dominated the press reports.

As a blogger and pro-nuclear activist, I wanted to know more about this so I could answer the opponents. The plant could *not* give me any information that it was not simultaneously giving to the press: it can't treat pro-nuclear reporters and bloggers preferentially. That would have been a disaster, many ways from Sunday. However, they could direct me to white papers by the Nuclear Energy Institute and to knowledgeable people there too. While the Institute might have balked at providing me (an individual) with tritium white papers in any quantity for handouts, the Institute was happy enough to send me stacks of white papers when the plant asked them to share information with me.

Well, this is the way it is when you are an activist. Your information from official sources may be helpful, but it will be partial. You are going to have to find many of your experts on your own, though the plant may be some help. The plant will especially be helpful in obtaining materials that are available to the public, but a bit expensive for you to copy.

More experts

SO, WHERE ARE THE EXPERTS? If you see pro-nuclear letters in the paper, contact those who wrote them. By following up on letters in the newspaper, I was able to contact many pro-nuclear people. In this way, I met a toxicology professor, a chemical engineer, several people who had retired from the nuclear plant, and many others who were also willing to help. Another source of experts is the American Nuclear Society, which has been developing a "speakers list" on various topics. Contact them. The Nuclear Energy Institute also has a third-party experts list: contact them too. (I'm on their list.) The Health Physics Society can be another resource.

The American Nuclear Society has a "Nuclear in the States" initiative.[23] The Society has a Toolkit for each state, and they will be updating the Toolkits regularly. The Toolkits are an excellent resource for local activists, and I look forward to the updates.

The Nuclear Energy Institute's SmartBrief is a very helpful resource to stay in the know on national and international nuclear news. It's a daily email blast of nuclear news from news outlets around the world, as well as information directly from the Institute itself, and it's free. To sign up, go to www.smartbrief.com, click "Get Newsletters," select "Energy & Chemicals," then "NEI SmartBrief." From there, you'll enter your email address and answer some easy questions about yourself.

You can also join the Nuclear Advocacy Network. This is a combination news bulletin and action alert. For example, I recently received an email from them about a new bill in Congress related to licensing advanced nuclear plants. The email described why this was important and gave a very simple action on how to support the bill. Anyone can join the Nuclear Advocacy Network, and you can follow them on Facebook. Visit http://www.nuclearadvocacynetwork.org/default.aspx to sign up.

Then there are somewhat less well-known groups, such as The Breakthrough Institute, a pro-nuclear environmentalist group. This relatively new group also has people to contact and position papers you can obtain.[24]

If you live near a college or community college with a nuclear program, you are in luck. Some community colleges (especially those near nuclear plants) offer an associate degree in Nuclear Engineering Technology. You may be able to get speakers from the program, and you may be able to get young people to support you during rallies and so forth. The professors, the students, the books, and the course materials can all be great resources for you.

Another resource is Facebook. I recommended Facebook? Yes. I did. Getting pro-nuclear ducks in order is a bit of a hit-or-miss situation. As I write this, there are some excellent groups such as "Fukushima Myth-Busters," and "Answers to Anti-Nuclear Memes," as well as more traditional pro-nuclear groups of various types. If you are supporting thorium reactors, you are especially in luck: just search for "thorium" on Facebook and you will find a treasure trove of sites. I suggest following groups like American Nuclear Society, Nuclear Energy Institute, World Nuclear Association, The Breakthrough Institute, and Nuclear Advocacy Network. The Nuclear Regulatory Commission is on Facebook, too.

Accuracy is important

BEING A PRO-NUCLEAR ADVOCATE IS HARD. An anti-nuclear speaker can get away with saying there are sixteen fish in the Connecticut River. A pro-nuclear speaker, on the other hand, has to have a message that will hold up under scrutiny. Accuracy is important.

But wait . . . can you get help from the power plant, even as little help as receiving copies of position papers from NEI? Won't you be a shill?

No. You won't be a shill. I feel strongly about this. The nuclear opponents will call you a shill no matter *what* you do, just because you support nuclear energy and nuclear technology. It's hard, but you just have to let those words roll off your back. You are not supporting nuclear because Mephistopheles showed up one evening and bought your soul. You are supporting nuclear because it is the right thing to do.

ACTION ITEM:

Get social. If you are on Facebook, join a pro-nuclear group and follow the discussion. Look on your local facility's website, and find out who the contact people are.

CHAPTER SEVEN

ACTIVISM FROM BEHIND YOUR COMPUTER

THERE ARE MANY WAYS to be an activist, starting at your desk and going up (in levels of visibility and commitment) through various forms of speaking and appearing in public. I think there are anti-nuclear activists who started by getting themselves in front of the public: holding rallies and vigils and so forth. However, most pro-nuclear activists are a bit shyer. Most of us are going to ease into this business more slowly. So let's start where most of us will start: sitting in front of our computers.

Note: I know that I am sitting in *front* of my computer, but sometimes I feel like I am *hiding behind* it. That's how I named the chapter.

Activism at your computer: Comments on websites

NOW THAT YOU HAVE A FEW statements ready to go . . . now what?

Let's start at your computer. First of all, hopefully you have some friends with whom to exchange emails about nuclear subjects that interest you and articles about nuclear that bother you. Keep track of those email exchanges, perhaps save them to a "nuclear stuff" folder on your computer. Because these exchanges were not a waste of time: they are golden raw data for the next step.

Now you have some speaking points and some email exchanges, which have supported you in what you are saying, and improved how you are saying it. Time to move forward.

You are in a target-rich environment. You may not have noticed this before, but you are.

You don't want to keep your wisdom to yourself. The easiest thing to do is to go on to the website of your local newspaper (if they allow comments) and find an article about energy to comment about. It might be an article about nuclear energy, or it might be an article about energy in general. Write a comment on it. You can write a small comment and feel very good about being "out there" and adding a rational voice to the discussion. You commented in public, but you also know that not everyone reads the comment stream. You have stepped forward, but not too far.

You can feel good about this, and it will not have taken much time.

Of course, opponents will comment on your comment, and you have to be ready for that. But you will discover that it isn't so bad. If they say something about you yourself, you can simply add a comment such as, "When someone writes something like this, I always assume the person can't refute what I said, so they descend to writing insults."

On the other hand, you don't have to write anything in reply to personal attacks. I believe that these attack-dog types are only credible to people who are already their supporters.

And speaking of supporters, remember those pro-nuclear people you are emailing with? Send them a link to what you wrote online. Thank them for supporting you and helping you refine your message.

At the minimum, you will get notes from your friends saying "great, well-done" and so forth. And you will feel good about what you did.

And perhaps some of your friends, emboldened by your bravery, will also comment on the article. Then you can comment on their comments and so forth, and you will sound like a major chorus of voices.

Congratulations. You have successfully completed your first activism!

Levels of comments

THERE ARE MANY TYPES OF COMMENTS. Pro-nuclear activism is a set of choices, and the important thing is to comment, to get your voice out there.

Complex, well-referenced comments: I have a friend who writes long, technical comments that show that the other person's assumptions about energy or pollution are wrong. This is a good thing to do. But don't feel you have to write a mini-thesis (as he does) to write a comment.

These comments are great for informing people, but I am not sure that many people read such comments all the way to the end. Sometimes a short and slightly witty comment will be read more. We need both types of comments out there.

Short and witty: Here's an example of a short and witty comment. When a judge ruled in favor of Vermont Yankee, one opponent commented on the article with a slam on the judge. The opponent claimed the ruling was just plain wrong, and the judge had conflicts of interest, etc., etc.

One excellent pro-nuclear comment replied to this anti-judge slam. The pro-nuclear comment was only about two sentences long.

The pro-nuclear person said that the judge's ruling had been carefully argued and was correct. The next sentence said that the man who was attacking the judge would have nominated the judge for sainthood, if the judge had ruled the other way. (In other words, this wasn't about a judge's conflict of interest . . . it was the anti-nuclear commenter expressing sour grapes.)

Two sentences. This short comment also got the pro-nuclear view in front of the public. Research and calculations were not required.

ACTION ITEM:

Be vocal. Find a nuclear-related article online and comment on it, then share the comment with your friends.

CHAPTER EIGHT

MORE ACTIVISM FROM BEHIND YOUR COMPUTER OR AT YOUR DESK

Rising up from the comment stream: Letters to the editor

AFTER YOU HAVE COMMENTED ON some articles and letters to the editor, you will be filled with a desire to get out in front of the comment stream rather than just joining the stream. You will want to say your own truth, rather than always be reacting to what someone else said. In other words, you are going to want to write your own letter to the editor.

It is easy to write a letter to the editor, and yet very few people actually do it. When you read your local newspaper, you will notice that the same people constantly get published in the letters column. This is simply because these people write to the letters column. For a modest-sized newspaper, that is all it takes. (If you want to write to the *New York Times*, on the other hand, getting published is considerably harder.)

Local newspapers

THE WONDERFUL THING ABOUT letters to the editor in a local newspaper is that so many people read the letters. My friends always notice each other's letters on any subject. People in my husband's chorus group have told me that they liked my letter . . . people whom I know only peripherally. In contrast, only a subset of people mix it up in the comments section online: you can write the most amazing stuff online, and nobody in your spouse's chorus group is going to see it.

Which is one of the reasons that you might start your activism at the online-comments level and get your feet wet, so to speak.

By the way, a "small" newspaper is a relative term. I prefer the term "local."

Some friends of mine were frustrated at how rarely their letters got published in their big city newspaper (the *Los Angeles Times*, as a matter of fact) and were somewhat scornful of their ability to get letters published in "small" newspapers so easily. I encouraged them to look up the circulation of these newspapers. The circulations were all in the mid-ten-thousands range. And don't scorn free papers, either. Many of them carry the truly local news, and some have letters sections.

Local newspapers are carefully read. When you get your letter in a local newspaper, thousands of people will read it. In comparison, your website comment on an article in any newspaper is likely to be read by at most a couple hundred people who have the time and interest to wade through the comments section of the website itself. (Probably read by more like fifty people IMHO, but that is just a guess. Newspapers must publish their circulation numbers, for the benefit of advertisers. Websites have no such requirements.)

Now that your feet are wet, however, it's time to plunge into the letters section of the local paper.

The letter itself

THE FIRST THING you are going to notice is that you have to keep it short. Most letters *must* be less than 300 words. Your chances of being published will go up as your word count goes down.

Oddly enough, the best advice I have found on writing letters to the editor is on the website of the anti-nuclear organization, Union of Concerned Scientists. (If they read this, they will surely say that that are *not* anti-nuclear. However, in my memory, they have never met a nuclear project that they considered safe enough for them to endorse. Well, enough about those guys.) Here's a blend of their advice, mine, and insight from my friend Guy Page, communications director at Vermont Energy Partnership and a former newspaper owner.

1. Make only one point. You may want to say that a local nuclear project will save money and protect the environment. You are better off making a good argument on *one* of those points, rather than unsubstantiated declarative sentences about both points.

2. Make it local. People read local papers to keep up with local events. If you can react to something published in the same paper as you are writing to, that is the best

strategy. If you are starting a new topic, tie it to local interests: "The closing of nuclear plants in neighboring states has led to more fossil fuels on the grid, which will affect our air quality."

3. Start strong. State the issue and your conclusion within the first two sentences if you possibly can. Don't make them guess what you are talking about.

4. Make it personal. Do you have a special expertise in the subject you are discussing? Expertise does not mean a Ph.D. in some relevant discipline (though if you have a Ph.D., do mention it). Expertise could be a related area or life experience: "Having grown up in coal country, I am delighted to support clean, soot-free nuclear plants." That is expertise. It's more important that your letter be personal (a *person* with certain life experiences is writing this letter) than that you have some type of academic credentials.

5. Make it short.

6. Send all emails in plain text. No attachments, no HTML. Many newspapers delete attachments without opening. There's too much malware out there. Plain text gets opened and looks professional.

7. Avoid sentence fragments, sections in ALL CAPS, and double exclamation marks!! Make your submission readable and adult.

And, of course, follow the newspaper's guidelines for sending in the letter, including your address and phone number, or whatever the newspaper requires. My local newspaper calls me to ask if I wrote the letter. It's a quick call, and I expect it.

The importance of friends

IT IS NORMAL TO BE worried when you first send a letter to a newspaper. Heck, it is normal to be worried even after you have years of experience in sending letters. "When I send this, will I make an almighty fool of myself? In public?" You can't help but think something like this.

This is why I started this book with information about finding friends and community. You need a friend to look over your letter. In the evening in which I am writing this first draft of this chapter, I have also done a quick edit on a letter that a friend plans to submit. Two days ago, another friend sent me a major blog post to review. I am writing an op-ed now, and I have two people lined up to look at it. In my opinion, a person simply cannot do this work alone.

When the Sierra Club decided to write letters against Vermont Yankee, they gathered their "experts" and held a series of letter-writing meetings at local libraries. They announced the meetings in the newspapers. In a similar methodology, several people at Vermont Yankee would gather to write letters in favor of the plant, on their own time, and review each other's letters.

In other words, you can review each other's work in person (more fun) or by email. The important thing is that you don't have to do this alone.

ACTION ITEM:

First draft. Write about 200 words in support of your nuclear facility. Email them to a friend and ask their opinion. Consider using these words as a letter to the editor.

CHAPTER NINE

ADVANCED LETTER WRITING: THE TRICKS OF THE TRADE

Now, for the tricks of the trade: building your media list and beginning to write op-eds.

The media list

Once you have put all that time and energy into writing that letter, you can get more mileage out of it with comparatively little work.

Look at the newspapers near you: the weeklies, the dailies, perhaps some local-interest websites that have an "opinion" section but don't print on paper. For example, we have an online investigative reporting site in Vermont: VTDigger, operated by the not-for-profit Vermont Journalism Trust. It has a commentary section. Similarly, some political sites have a place for letters. You have to figure out your own community.

Local newspapers are important: find them. These newspapers are often the only source of local news, and people read them avidly. A moderate circulation weekly newspaper in Vermont (*Seven Days*) has a print run of 35,000. The daily *San Luis Obispo Tribune* (in California) has a similar circulation. The *Rutland Herald*, a daily Vermont paper, has a circulation of about 12,000. Unlike the bigger papers such as the *Los Angeles Times*, these papers are read cover to cover by their readership.

So, first you need to do some research. Go to the websites of the various newspapers and get the addresses of where you are supposed to send letters to the editors. Make a list of eight addresses or more. (There are that many possibilities everywhere.) Also read the guidelines of the letters to the editors in these newspapers. They are usually the same all over: you have to have written the letter yourself, you have to put your address and your phone number at the bottom of the letter, it has to be less than 300 words.

But if there is another requirement, make a note of it. For example, one newspaper in Massachusetts requires that any letter *only* appear in that newspaper. You may want to leave that newspaper off your list . . . or you may want to make a note of it, and do a slightly different version of each letter to send to them.

(Sneaky trick. If you know someone in public relations in your area, your friend may be willing to share their "media list" with you. Don't expect they will share it, but they might . . . Or, someone who works with the nuclear facility might be willing to look over your list and make further suggestions. You are not alone. Remember that.)

At any rate, now you have a list of letters-to-the-editor email addresses, and they all have similar guidelines. (Because if they had special guidelines, you have dropped them or put them on a different list.) Now, get your letter ready to send—and this is key:

Put your own address in the "to" line. Put your media email list in the bcc (blind copy) line. As a friend of mine explained to me:

The editors *know* you are sending it to more than one place, but they don't like to have this shoved in their face. It's a courtesy to send it bcc when you are sending to many places.

(Who knew editors were so sensitive? But in any case, do it.)

Note that most email programs will not allow you to send to a huge bcc list, for fear you are spamming. If you have only eight or a dozen people on your media list, you are good with bcc. If you begin getting tons of people on your list (more than about fifteen) you will be safest dividing the list into two lists and sending two emails.

This whole thing sounds hard, but it isn't. You do some online research for an hour or so, *once*. You put together an email list, *once*. And from then on, all your letters go to many newspapers, and get many readers. Of course, eventually, some addresses will change or you may get some bounces, but fixing this is pretty straightforward, because you have a pretty short list anyhow.

Editorial writing: You need a history or a platform

AFTER I HAD WRITTEN LETTERS for quite a few years, my local newspaper asked me to write op-eds. You can write op-eds right off the bat, of course, but it is unlikely they will be published unless you are:

- Already known to the editor (lots of letters to the editor)
- Have a platform

What is a platform? A platform is being well known in some way. Perhaps you have a well-read local blog. Perhaps you have joined or formed some type of pro-nuclear group. At one point, the American Nuclear Society (a professional organization) wanted to encourage pro-nuclear activities by its members. Howard Shaffer agreed to be their "test case," so to speak, and was therefore able to sign his letters and op-eds as "Project Leader, American Nuclear Society Vermont Pilot Project." Perhaps you have been in front of crowds of real people, speaking about energy or debating anti-nuclear speakers. In that case, you can be "with twenty years' experience in the industry [if you have this] and a frequent speaker on nuclear energy." I myself joined the Ethan Allen Institute, a local libertarian think tank that was in favor of keeping Vermont Yankee open. At that point, I could and did introduce myself as Director, Energy Education Project of the Ethan Allen Institute.

It is important that what you say about yourself is true: integrity is key. However, you don't have to be a former commissioner of the NRC to have a platform. Many things can give you a platform. Before granting you all that precious space in the newspaper (and it *is* precious and very much a subject of competition) for an op-ed, the editor needs to know who you are and if you have some standing. Be ready to explain yourself, in terms of your background and your platform.

Your platform may be considered to be very specific. For example, I am pretty much acknowledged to be an expert on energy issues in the Northeast, and especially in nuclear energy. I have a platform for that. If I decided to write an op-ed about nuclear energy worldwide, it would be much harder to get published.

This happened with a friend of mine whose father works at the local nuclear plant. He began writing letters to the editor while he was still in high school, and he was published frequently. He was definitely considered to be an expert on the emotional and economic effects of the continuing operation or possible shutdown of the power plant.

However, at one point, he did a great deal of research on China, the role of engineers in Chinese society, and the history of the Three Gorges Dam and the Chinese nuclear energy program. He wrote a very interesting article on the history of Chinese technical policies, but could not get it published. He didn't have a platform for expertise on China. I think he would have had to be an NRC commissioner or a member of the State Department in order to get such a high-level article published.

However, he was co-blogger on a major blog, and he published his article on that blog.[25]

Which brings us to social media, and why I think people should be blogging, using Facebook, tweeting, and so forth. But that is covered in a later chapter.

ACTION ITEM:

Find local newspapers. Make a list of five local newspapers, including free newspapers and local weeklies. Research their letters to the editor policy.

CHAPTER TEN

PETITIONS AND PERSEVERANCE

YOU MAY BE THINKING by now that nuclear advocacy is a lot of work, and do you really want to get involved in all this? It can be done, and by people just like you.

Before we get into social media activism, I would like you to read the history that Marie-Christine Hupé, a young woman from Quebec, shared with me about her actions to save the Gentilly 2 nuclear power plant in the fall of 2012.

A candidate for premier announced that, if elected, she would close Gentilly 2. Hupé circulated a petition and collected more than 10,000 signatures of people who were against permanently closing the plant. Through her journey, Hupé met with elected officials, gave countless media interviews, and helped organize a solidarity march before delivering her petition to the National Assembly in Quebec City. This is her story.

Marie-Christine Hupé and the Gentilly Petitions (by Mlle. Hupé)

Native from the region and temporary employee at Hydro Québec, I was witnessing our town's downfall, as for the past few years, many companies closed in the region; many plants with many employees were closing one after another. So for the economy of the region, this was catastrophic. When I heard this, I couldn't stay indifferent . . . I then turned to a reporter friend, thinking he could guide me in the right direction, as I had never done a petition before and I didn't know where to start.

Marie-Christine Hupé collecting signatures for Gentilly 2, Trois-Rivieres Quebec, September 12, 2012

Credit: Francois Gervais

The next evening, Mrs. Marois was elected as Premier of Quebec, and she in fact announced the official shutdown of the plant. So I had to speed up the petition process. The same day, my reporter friend invited me to his radio show. The interview lasted 30 minutes and that was the start of a crazy story for me.

After my interview, I met our deputy (Deputy Premier of Quebec) who wanted to [support me]. Then I met the mayor and two area Chambers of Commerce . . . That day, I gave at least twenty media interviews. I was really proud to know the people of my area were behind me.

After putting my petition on paper, I went to strategic locations to collect signatures. Many people joined me to get more signatures. Also, I often visited the employees of the plant to keep them informed of my progress. It was important for me as [plant employees] were the first ones affected by all this and the last ones informed. For me, it was a nonsense.

Later, Hupé was contacted and advised that the National Assembly had rejected her petition because it wasn't standard and was inadmissible. It had 4,000 signatures.

I am only a citizen who is worried about the future of her area and who took the lead to help make things happen . . . I was so angry at the situation that I couldn't abandon it because in my mind, that's what the government wanted. So I worked harder, and with the help of my deputy, we created a petition with a legal standard and admissible text, and I continued to get signatures. After a few days, the Assembly reversed its decision about the first petition: it would be non-standard but admissible! First victory for me: they wouldn't take me down!

I was then invited to many meetings with some elected officials, business managers, engineers, and many people who were affected in some way by the plant's closure. It was a roundtable to help us find a solution.

We organized a solidarity march for Gentilly 2. That day was memorable and emotional for me. I had been working so hard, and seeing all those people present moved me. There were thousands of activists. We walked from Bécancour to the plant, which means a walk of about ten kilometers. People were supposed to walk on the bicycle path beside the road but they decided otherwise: they walked directly on the road and blocked it in order to get visibility . . . During that wonderful day, people brought me sheets filled with signatures and congratulated me for my involvement. It was heartwarming, and it was a wonderful reward.

Subsequently, I was invited to many debates, TV and radio shows, often as spectator, but sometimes as guest . . . My reporter friend helped me a lot as I was on the radio with him every day (sometimes twice) during the first weeks of my petition.

After that, I was on air at least once a week. That was my moment to say where I would be to get signatures, which helped reach a lot more people. I also used Facebook a lot to promote where I would be (you can easily go on my Facebook profile to find some pictures, newspaper articles, and radio interviews—in French, of course).

The deposit date for my petition was November 28, 2012. On November 28, I was on my way to the National Assembly in Quebec City to deposit my two petitions that amounted to almost 10,000 signatures, collected since September 19.

I lived that day as a deputy since I was following our deputy everywhere. I witnessed the questions period, and then the deposit of my two petitions. After the deposit, the deputy presented me to the deputies and ministers. They all stood and applauded me for a long time, which was for me one of the best rewards I could get from this experience.

That experience will remain forever etched in my mind. It was a period of my life filled with emotions, growth, and learning. We quickly forget what we did in the past, and sharing it with you makes me realize all the hard work I did and that without all those people, I wouldn't have made it. Thank you.

Mlle. Hupé's story was originally shared in French, her native language.

ACTION ITEM:

What obstacle to your advocacy needs some more perseverance? There are situations where starting a petition is worthwhile. This was one of them: the power plant supporters won national attention. Though the plant was shut down, nobody could claim that this was "of course what should have happened." There were too many protests, and too many signatures, and the needle moved toward nuclear.

However, Mlle. Hupé's story is far more important than the petition itself. It shows the importance of perseverance, the ability of one person to make a difference, and what it takes to overcome anti-nuclear and bureaucratic obstacles.

Ask yourself: "In my own advocacy, in what area should I be more forceful in applying my energy and enthusiasm?"

NUCLEAR ENERGY SAFETY

I DON'T WANT TO CALL THIS section "Nuclear Energy Safety."
I want to call it "Ordinary Nuclear Energy."

The problem with "safety" is that the very word implies
danger. I don't say, "Let's go to the farmers market—it's perfectly safe!" But a wilderness instructor might tell me, "You
will be able to rappel down this cliff. It's really quite safe!"
You see what I mean about the word "safe"?

However, I think someone would think I was being too-
cute by using any word besides "safety." So there the word is,
right in this white-paper title.

Bottom line: per kWh produced, nuclear is the safest form of
electricity production available.

What will we do with the waste?

I OFTEN MENTION THE FACT that I left the renewable group
and joined the nuclear group at the Electric Power Research
Institute (EPRI). Unfortunately, this gives the impression that

my support of nuclear energy had a "road to Damascus" conversion involved. That isn't quite the way it happened.

I had pretty much convinced myself that nuclear was a better option than fossil fuels for the air and for people's health: that opinion came from my experience with NOx control. And I was sure that nuclear was a more realistic option than renewables, which made very little power: that opinion came from my work in the renewables group. But I wasn't quite satisfied with nuclear. My issue: what will we do with the waste?

This was a long time ago. Nowadays, I would just have referred myself to Gwyneth Craven's excellent book *Power to Save the World*. Section five of her book, "Closing the Circle," describes her careful investigations into the reality of dealing with nuclear waste. However, when I had joined the nuclear group at EPRI, Cravens hadn't written her book yet. So I was forced to figure this out for myself.

Well, yes, I was at EPRI, in the nuclear group, so I could ask my colleagues. And I asked them. However, most of the people in the nuclear group were simply sure that the waste was "no problem." I felt they didn't appreciate my questions. My questions were just proving that I was the "woman from the renewables group." (Not one of our crowd.)

No. There was not a conversion experience for me. So I stopped asking people. After a while, I did begin to figure it out for myself.

I have concluded that the good thing about nuclear waste is that there is so little of it, it is so easy to contain, and it doesn't last long.

So little: A simple comparison. I visited Merrimack Station, a 440-MW coal plant in New Hampshire.[26] This station uses the equivalent of 40 coal cars a day, supplied by rail or barge. Each car is 100 tons of coal. Assuming the coal is 10 percent ash, the plant will produce 400 tons of ash per day. *Four coal cars of ash, per day.* (Actually, this is unfair to Merrimack Station, which is set up to produce more slag than ash. But the tonnage of ash-plus-slag is the same.) In contrast, Vermont Yankee was 600 MW, and it used three semi-trucks' worth of fuel every 18 months! Quite a difference in disposal needs, between hundreds of tons a day and three semis every eighteen months.

So easy to contain: ceramics (fuel rods) are easier to handle than powdery fly ash or fly ash in a liquid slurry or gases going up into the air.

If someone said to me: You are going to have to handle an industrial by-product that is somewhat hazardous. In what form do you want it? Do you want it as a gas, a liquid, a slurry, or finely divided ash? Or maybe you want it as ceramic? Which do you think would be easiest to handle?

Obviously, I would want the ceramic.

Used nuclear fuel is a ceramic. The ceramic is neatly contained inside a pool of water or in concrete canisters at the nuclear plant. It does not infiltrate waterways or the air.

So short-lived: The fact is that nuclear radiation *has* a half-life. The radiation goes away. It ends. As a general rule, the longer the half-life, the less dangerous the material. I discuss this on my blog, but I'll restate it here because it is so important and it comes up so often.

A nuclear opponent will write that an isotope in spent fuel "has an immensely long half-life." (Fill in a number. For example, 700 million years for uranium 235 or 373,000 years for plutonium 242.) They claim this long half-life means the isotope will be dangerous forever. That the isotope is a horrible legacy for our children, etc.

Actually, a long half-life means that the isotope is not very dangerous, right now. And will be less dangerous in the future.

Let's look at what a "long half-life" means. Say I had one hundred atoms of an isotope with a ten-minute half-life. By the definition of "half-life," fifty of those atoms would release radioactivity in a ten-minute period. That would be a comparatively high release of radioactivity in a short time.

Now imagine I have one hundred atoms of an isotope with a ten-year half-life. Again by the definition of half-life, fifty atoms would release radioactivity over a period of ten years. In other words, every few months, one atom would release some radioactivity, and a few months later, another atom would decay. An isotope with a ten-year half-life is far less radioactive than an isotope with a ten-minute half-life.

An isotope with a million-year half-life is not a very radioactive isotope at all. The claim "radioactive for millions of years" is scary sounding, but it doesn't indicate high levels of danger, now or in the future.

If you want to talk about scary, however, think about mercury in coal fly ash. The mercury has a half-life of infinity. It just never goes away.

However, the basic problem is not that the mercury lasts forever. It's the containment problem again. If the mercury were a ceramic that would stay in one place—but it's not. Mercury in a coal plant is hard to contain, because much of it is in gaseous form, and some is also chemically bound into powdery fly ash. Being hard to contain, mercury enters the biosphere relatively easily. However, progress is being made at reducing mercury emissions.

Interestingly, though we started by talking about mercury as permanent (infinite half-life, not radioactive), we are back to the advantage that nuclear fuel has by being a ceramic. If mercury from coal plants were a ceramic, it would be much less dangerous. There are many dangerous substances in the world. But some (nuclear fuel, for example) are easy to isolate from the biosphere. And some (mercury, for example) are not so easy to isolate.

Geeky side note about coal use. I remembered that the people at Merrimack Station mentioned 40 coal cars a day, but I was uncomfortable writing this verbally-received number in this book, so I checked it using Energy Administration heat rates for coal plants, heat content of bituminous coal, etc. Basically, 40 cars per day is the right number, assuming the plant runs all day.

However, since the capacity factor of coal plants is around 60 percent,[27] I should probably have said something like: this plant requires 40 cars of coal to run for a full day. Clearly, it doesn't use fuel when it is not running.

We can use the used fuel, too

ONCE AGAIN, THIS COULD BE a book in itself. It is worth pointing out that the used nuclear fuel is still a valuable material. It can be used directly in some types of reactors (CanDu, Breeder reactors), and make even more power from the same fuel rods. The plutonium in the used fuel can be separated (I saw this done on a trip to France). Next, the plutonium oxide can be mixed with uranium oxide. The resulting mixed-oxide fuel, MOX, is used in reactors in Europe and Japan.

When I review the various processes for re-using nuclear fuel, they don't strike me as particularly dangerous. But maybe that is because I'm a chemist. I'm used to the idea that many types of manufacturing, including making plastics, aluminum, and semiconductors, are chemical processes that require careful handling. Re-using nuclear fuel also requires care. Not "more care than anything else." It is not a uniquely dangerous process.

In other words, as a by-product that needs disposal, spent nuclear fuel is in an easy-to-handle form. Depending on the fuel cycle chosen, it may not need disposal at all. We may choose to use it again.

Radiation Releases

THE USED FUEL IS OF NO particular danger to people in the area. It is a safely contained, easy-to-contain ceramic. Okay. But what about the rest of the power plant? Is it safe to live near an operating nuclear plant? What about those radiation releases?

Most people who work at a power plant are quite happy to live near a power plant. They know a great deal about nuclear power, and they have no problem with their families living near the plant. But maybe they are prejudiced in favor of nuclear? To answer the question of "Is it safe to live near a nuclear plant?" I need to include some perspective.

Americans receive an average of 620 millirem of radiation per year. About half of this comes from natural background radiation—radon in the air, cosmic rays, and the earth itself. The other half comes from man-made sources, medical procedures like x-rays, CT scans, and bone scans.

A nuclear power plant also releases radioactivity: very little radioactivity. (Actually, coal plants release more radioactivity—all that ash. For a set of comparisons, look at the radioactive trace elements section of the Wikipedia article on coal.)[28]

If you lived within fifty miles of a nuclear power plant, you would receive an average extra radiation dose of about .01 millirem per year.[29] This is less radiation exposure than what you receive from your yearly dental x-ray. A dental x-ray gives a radiation dose of about 1.5 millirem.[30]

In general, the NRC has a policy of setting limits to ensure that the amount of radiation exposure from nuclear plants is only a fraction of normal background radiation exposure.

And what is background exposure? I only gradually learned how varied background exposure is. Live in a house a couple of hundred feet up a hill, and you get more cosmic radiation than in houses down in the valley. Live in a house built on granite, and you get more radiation than a house built on limestone. It is almost impossible to find a large-scale map of "background radiation," because the radiation varies so much between places that are fairly close together.

Total background radiation (from rocks and cosmic radiation) in the US has huge variations, depending on location. The highest levels of background radiation occur on the Colorado Plateau.[31] The NRC has an interactive page on calculating your own yearly exposure. Living in a brick building adds 7 millirem to your yearly radiation dose, while living near a nuclear plant adds 0.01 millirem.[32]

How deadly is your kilowatt?

JAMES CONCA, AT FORBES, WROTE "How Deadly Is Your Kilowatt?" In order to do a fair comparison between different technologies, he carefully assesses coal-energy-related deaths in China separately from such deaths in the rest of the world. Coal energy deaths in China are 170,000 deaths per trillion kWh, compared to 10,000 coal energy deaths per trillion kWh in the U.S. (For what it is worth, China also had the Banqiao hydro collapse, which killed 171,000 people in 1975. That definitely affects hydro power statistics. It might be better to look at "world statistics" and "China statistics" separately in many cases.)

Nuclear has the lowest global average with 90 deaths per trillion kWh.

In contrast, natural gas has 4,000 deaths per trillion kWh, worldwide. Wind has 150 deaths per trillion kWh.[33]

That's the bottom line, after all. I have personally worked on research projects to improve renewable power plants, fossil plants, and nuclear plants. As Conca shows in his article, nuclear is the safest way to make electricity.

CHAPTER ELEVEN

SOCIAL MEDIA. A BIGGER COMMUNITY—BUT LESS ENGAGED

ANOTHER TYPE OF ACTIVISM at your own desk is being active on social media. There are thousands of books and websites about how to use social media. As a matter of fact, name your platform (LinkedIn, Facebook) and there are probably hundreds of books about that platform. Besides books, there are websites, free seminars, pay-for-my-seminar, courses, etc.

I will not even attempt to duplicate this type of work in my chapter. The question is: What do *you* want to do with social media? Using social media will take many hours of your time: how will it help *your* pro-nuclear activism?

Most of the books about social media assume that you have something to sell. This could be a product or even advertising space on your blog. A product could include a set of seminars, etc. Social media training usually teaches you how to write grabbing headlines, create offers they can't refuse (well, offers they will have a hard time refusing), and increase your click rates. There's a whole new set of metrics available, my friend, just for talking about social media. But these metrics may not be your metrics.

Instead of reviewing the great and wonderful world of social media, I will explain how you can use it as an activist. There are only two ideas, and they are quite simple:

1. To reach and inform a larger audience, some of whom will be willing to join you in activism. You do this with Facebook and Twitter (and Pinterest and Reddit, but basically, the latter platforms are quite similar to Facebook and Twitter).

2. To keep a record of the issues and events around your nuclear facility and have a place to refer people who ask you questions. You do this with a blog.

Now, these are not totally clear-cut distinctions, of course. Facebook will keep a certain level of records (as your blog does), and your blog will reach and inform a larger audience (as Facebook does) than you reach when you give talks at local events and at local clubs. But let's talk about these ideas separately, acknowledging that there is sure to be overlap between the platforms.

In general, I have found that different people, and different groups of people, follow my writing on the two different types of platforms. Let's start with Facebook and Twitter.

Facebook and Twitter activism

BEFORE WE GET INTO HOW to be a nuclear activist on social media, let's remember *why* we are doing it.

The good news about Facebook and Twitter is that you can attract followers who would not follow you on other media. Also, the Facebook community can make you feel supported: people are listening to what you say. You can also find out a lot about what is happening in the nuclear world, and find it out very quickly. On Facebook and Twitter, I find links to pro-nuclear articles and rebuttals of anti-nuclear articles. Some articles of all kinds are mere opinion, but many articles are meticulously researched and provide links to original documents. Facebook and Twitter are tremendously valuable resources, especially for information on breaking news.

The bad news about Facebook and Twitter is that they can be shallow and self-referential. It tends to be the very same people following all the pro-nuclear sites and talking to each other. Of course, it is lovely to have Facebook friends all over the world. If I ever visit Australia, especially South Australia, I am looking forward to meeting some great people, face to face. However, most Facebook people are unlikely to come to rallies and so forth. They don't live nearby, for one thing. Also, many of them are Facebook devotees, not people who want to go out on the street and demonstrate, or even write a letter.

The role of Facebook in activism is a subject of academic research recently. For example, Pablo Barbera (et al.) wrote an article in the Public Library of Science: "The Critical Periphery in the Growth of Social Protests."[34] This article, published in 2015, includes authors from New York University, Oxford, and the Annenberg School for Communication at the University of Pennsylvania. The article describes the "core group" of active supporters for a cause, in contrast to social media "slacktivist" supporters. On the other hand, the paper concludes that social media followers can make up in numbers for what they lack in commitment, especially about national issues.

Please understand . . . there are exceptions. When the Public Service Board was holding hearings about Vermont Yankee, two Vermont people who follow my Save Vermont Yankee Facebook Page drove down to Vernon (over a hundred miles roundtrip) and made statements in favor of the plant. I had advertised the hearing on the page. Others wrote letters to the Public Service Board. And it is easier to do this now: there is a Call-to-Action choice for not-for-profit Facebook pages. So Facebook can find serious supporters.

The problem is the signal-to-noise ratio. You can have hundreds of followers on Facebook and only get a dozen who will support your work in any substantial way. A dozen is great: don't get me wrong. But you shouldn't spend all your time on social media, because it is not the most effective way to support your nuclear facility.

However, do have a Facebook page. Do post links on it fairly frequently. Do advertise . . . you can get lots of followers for an expenditure of maybe $20. But remember its limitations. Facebook and Twitter are wonderful for sharing information. However, Facebook pages are not necessarily activism.

Activism on Facebook

STILL, FACEBOOK CAN BE HELPFUL to the activist. In Facebook and Twitter activism, you can post many short notes, calls to action, and especially links about the nuclear facility you are supporting. Is there a television show that mentions something about the plant or a radio interview or a newspaper story? You can link to it.

How do you do this? Well, first you start a Facebook Page for your facility. It is best to name yourself as the administrator of the page and write something on the page to make sure nobody confuses your Facebook page with the company's own official Facebook page. This is easy. You can just say that this page is for friends and supporters of your plant. You have to make some visibility choices, but they aren't hard.

Why did I say a page instead of a group? Well, groups are good, too. However, I once was chief administrator for a Facebook group. It had 1,200 members, and Facebook told me they were dissolving that group, because group features are limited when a group reaches a certain size. I don't think pages have that requirement.

Also, people "like" pages, but they have to "join" a group. This can be equally easy . . . or not. Some groups require moderator approval before anyone joins. And so forth. Of course, you can set up the group the way you want it to be, but I find groups somewhat ambiguous.

For example, one thing I don't like about groups is that the moderator can add you to a group. This involuntary conscription into groups is known as "adding" someone to a group. I (involuntarily) became a member of a Facebook group with an amusing title that includes the word "Involuntary." That was okay with me: it is a fun group, despite being involuntary.

I have been less amused when I have found myself suddenly joined to quasi-political groups. I was on a mailing list to support a certain local candidate, and suddenly I was a member of a Facebook group for a not-for-profit that supported some of that candidate's positions. They just added me to the group. How did they know I supported the candidate because of those particular positions? As a matter of fact, I didn't support those positions. In my opinion, Facebook groups are a bit treacherous.

Sometimes people get involuntarily added to Facebook groups, and this causes chaos in their lives. A *Wall Street Journal* article describes a girl who went away to college, where she was finally able to admit that she was gay. She joined a gay chorus at the college. However, she was not yet "out" to her family and friends back home. Then the chorus director decided to form a Facebook group. He formed a nice, open visible group with an open members-list of everyone in the gay chorus. And that is how her parents found out she was gay. This led to the kind of difficulties and misery you might expect.[35]

Of course this was not a good move on the part of the chorus director! However, my point is that the girl could do nothing about it. The director added her to the Facebook group, and then she was "out" to the entire world. When I was joined to the not-for-profit group, everyone assumed I supported its mission.

One thing about a page: it is fully the choice of the person to like the page or not. I can't "add you" to my page. I "like" that. Liking is voluntary.

Also, moderating a group is somewhat harder than administering a page. On this, my information may be out of date. I encourage you to look into Facebook rules yourself and decide on a group or a page. Meanwhile, I will keep writing as if you have started a page.

Now you have a page

REMEMBER, THE POINT OF THE page is to supply people who "like" the page with *information* about the nuclear facility you are defending, and to be able to motivate them to take *action* when needed.

Information: In many cases, your page will be a valuable resource for pro-nuclear people to hear the "other side" of the news, since the Mainstream Media have a tendency to publish articles I would call "Scare story! Radiation might occur!"

Therefore, you want to have interesting, reliable information on your page. Where can you find it? One of the simplest ways to find information is to have a Google alert set for the name of the nuclear facility you support. About once a day, Google will send you an email alert. (You need to have a Gmail account to set a Google alert, but once you have that, it's easy to set the alert.)

The Google alert will send you an email with a series of links about your facility. Amazingly enough, each link has a little Facebook icon next to it, and that makes it very easy to post the link on your new page.

When you post it, say something about the link: other people and other pages will pick up what you say. This is worth doing. For example, an article titled "Court Turns Down State Challenge on Radiation Safety" can be linked, but you can write something a little more pro-nuclear to describe it: "State loses in court, after accusing the plant of radiation danger." Write a title that makes it clear why you are linking to this story. The article itself undoubtedly has lots of quotes from nuclear opponents, viewing with alarm the horrible decision the court made. The way you describe the article can make it clear that you support the court's decision.

I also suggest "liking" a couple of other pro-nuclear pages on Facebook: certainly the Facebook page of your plant, the American Nuclear Society page, and perhaps pages such as "Save Vermont Yankee" or "Mothers for Nuclear." You will find links on these pages which you can share on your page, and these links will please your readers and keep them coming back.

Facebook to Twitter

I HAD A FRIEND WRITE a program that automatically "tweets" my postings on Facebook to Twitter. This is another way to have followers. I'm not going to get very far into Twitter here, but it is another place where you can find followers, and it is another place where pro-nuclear information is quick and free. I suggest that being on Twitter can be very helpful in terms of obtaining information quickly (from relevant tweets) and does not have to be very time consuming. Many free services (such as Tweetdeck) will automate searching for you and keep the results in useful columns.

I can get down in the weeds about Facebook and Twitter strategies, but there are almost an infinite number of books for that.

Facebook page with Call to Action button

Action: Now, the action part of Facebook. You can urge people to take action by many methods. Facebook has a Call-to Action button. If you stage an event, you can invite the people who "like" your page to come to that event. If there is a petition to sign, link to it on Facebook. Link to it a couple of times at different times of the day: nobody is always on Facebook. A person gets on Facebook, and watches the stream go by. (The news feed.) You need to be on that stream more than once. You can also turn signing the petition into an "event," which is another way to notify people.

Facebook works pretty well for getting people to sign things. Facebook is the home of the simple click: "like," vote for, sign. When you want people to do more (testify at a hearing, write a letter to the editor), you need more than Facebook.

I think you need a blog, and that is what the next chapter is about. But meanwhile, back on Facebook . . .

Finding serious followers on Facebook

YOU WILL QUICKLY LEARN which people on Facebook are really engaged. When you link to a petition, these people will reply: "signed it." When you write a post, they will "like" it or (better yet) comment. Let me be blunt here:

You need to ask these people for their email addresses, so that they join you in more activism. I generally do that through the Private Message part of Facebook. Sometimes I ask them directly, sometimes I tell them why I want their email, and sometimes I send my email and ask if they can send me their email for my active list. Not everyone will give you the email address, but you have to try.

And now, on to blogging.

ACTION ITEM:

Join the conversation. Visit two pro-nuclear Facebook pages that you identified at the end of chapter 6. Leave a comment on one of them.

CHAPTER TWELVE

BLOGGING

I THINK THAT WRITING a blog is one of the most important ways to use social media. Indeed, if your time is limited, I would say you should write a blog, and perhaps just *read* Twitter and Facebook for information. If there is only one social media thing you plan to do, I suggest . . . a blog.

I started my own blog when I realized I was writing lengthy emails to my friends about Vermont Yankee. These letters covered newspaper articles about Vermont Yankee and described hearings I attended about Vermont Yankee. I was also commenting on pro-nuclear blogs, sharing what I knew about Vermont Yankee, etc. On New Year's Eve 2010, I decided I wanted a better record of all this work. Not just emails and comments. Somewhere where I would discuss Vermont Yankee, very specifically. And I started my blog on January 1, 2010.

Why am I so in favor of blogging? There are many websites, books, and programs about "how to blog effectively." What I want to write about here is *why* an activist should blog.

Five Reasons to Have a Blog

HERE ARE MY REASONS:

1. Blogs are a visible and complete way to present the local pro-nuclear side of the story.
2. Blogs attract people who are interested in the topic. These people are more likely to invest time in activities that support the local plant.
3. You can use a blog post as a very effective call to action, on Facebook and other media.
4. Blogs attract reporters (you become an expert).
5. Blogs have staying power.

I consider my blog a very important part of my support of nuclear energy. In particular, blogs are a very effective way to motivate local people. Many people who have joined in writing letters, speaking before the Public Service Board, and so forth, found out about the events through the blog.

Blogs take advantage of a marketing phenomenon called "self-selection." If a person heads for the organic coffee section of the supermarket, that person has self-selected as a person who is willing to pay more for high-quality coffee. You don't have to advertise or convince that person that it is worth the money to pay more for good coffee. They are already convinced.

Similarly, if someone is following a blog about a local nuclear facility, that person is more than halfway ready to write a letter, join a demonstration, or write a comment to a governmental agency during an open-comment period.

Well, enough of a prologue about why blogs are more likely to help activism than Facebook.

Side note: I am sure somebody is going to ask me why I didn't start a web site instead of a blog. There are various long answers, but the main thing is that web pages become out of date, don't follow current events easily, and eventually people stop reading them. In contrast, people follow blogs. (In my opinion, a well-designed web site should include a blog.)

1) Blogs for presentation of the pro-nuclear side of the story

Many newspapers have an almost reflexive fear of nuclear energy and are often slanted anti-nuclear in their articles. Plus, reporters are supposed to get both sides of the story (which is a good thing), but that often means that they interview someone at the power plant. This spokesman gives a careful and unemotional statement. Then the reporter goes on to interview a local anti-nuclear activist, who describes fire, brimstone, and imminent destruction. The reporter does not evaluate the two statements or make any comments about their veracity. The "he-said, she-said" reporting leaves the reader remembering fire and brimstone. The message is: Be afraid, be very afraid!

And that is the scenario that takes place *if* the reporter is honest and serious. Things can be much worse. Some reporters are so slanted against nuclear that they don't even know they are slanted. Or maybe they know they are slanted but they don't care. I could give some flagrant examples, but let me just give one example that happened to me.

For a while, while Vermont Yankee was running, I wrote op-eds for the local paper about Vermont energy issues. These op-eds went through an editor, of course. After she edited the op-ed, she would send it back to me for final approval. Thank heavens for that last step! To my astonishment, my op-ed (as edited) described Vermont Yankee as "the troubled plant." That came from her mind, not my op-ed. Well, I made sure that did not stay in the final version. However, that is a very mild (but telling) example of how nuclear energy is described, even when the article (as written by me) is an opinion piece and very positive.

Okay. I could have an entire chapter of examples, much worse than this, of how nuclear energy is described in the press.

Pro-nuclear people, or people who actually work at or are knowledgeable about the facility, know that what's printed in the press is often exaggerated and not always the full truth. They are often eager to have a place where they can read their side of the story, or contribute to accurate conversations on the issue.

For example, at Vermont Yankee, the people at the plant had named the local newspaper, the *Brattleboro Reformer*, the "Misinformer," because it had an anti-nuclear editorial policy and frequently ran stories that seemed more in line with the editorial policy than they needed to be.

In your blog, you can comment on negative stories and tell positive stories. For example, at one point, the opponents were acting as if a tritium leak at Vermont Yankee (a leak which was never even detectable in any well that was not on the plant site) was about to poison all the children in Vermont. However, in my blog, "Yes Vermont Yankee," I could write facts and comparisons about tritium. This sort of thing is worth doing. The people who support nuclear will appreciate it. And this leads directly to point two:

2) Blogs attract people who may be interested in activism

The most important people you want to attract are local people. Because you are giving "their" point of view, pro-nuclear people of all kinds will read your blog. When people have come with me to hearings and demonstrations, most of them were regular readers of my blog.

Also, your blog can literally be a voice for local people. For example, I discovered that one man who read my blog was a chemist, a very knowledgeable fisherman, and the founder of a river-support environmental group. I asked him to write some guest posts on my blog: they were terrific posts. He might have written letters to the editor (and he did); but on the blog, he had time and scope to explain the mechanics of why mercury in fish remains a far bigger problem than any conceivable effect of tritium.

Another man often commented on my blog, and I asked him to write a guest post comparing nuclear with fossil fuels. Then there was the entire "voices for Vermont Yankee" part of my blog, where I printed the statements people had made in favor of Vermont Yankee during a hearing before the Public Service Board. Eventually, my husband and I compiled a book *Voices for Vermont Yankee.*

As I wrote above, about self-selection, blogs attract people willing to invest the time to read the blog and are truly interested in helping nuclear power.

What about non-local people? For your activism, local people are the ones that you are most interested in attracting, but non-local people who comment on your blog are also extremely valuable. They are often quite knowledgeable, and they will supplement the information on your blog. You will get some of the best suggestions, from very knowledgeable people, about your local situation. This helps make you a stronger advocate. Plus, the presence of pro-nuclear advocates from around the world is quite reassuring to you, yourself. I find that my blog gives me a great deal of emotional support, just by the readership and the comments.

3) Blog posts can be effective calls to action

The wonderful thing about a blog post as a call to action is that it can contain all the separate things you often need in a call-to-action: a reason, an action, and an example.

If you want people to write the NRC during an open-comment period, for example, you would want to say what the issue is, supply a link to where they should submit comments, and (very important) write an example.

It's hard to do all this in a short format (like Twitter or Facebook). Something will be shortchanged in the short formats. However, the short formats are more effective with the blog as a link.

For example, if I didn't have a blog, on Facebook, I might write something like:

"Time to write the NRC a comment about the no-safe-dose rule. Link here to NRC website for the comments."

In contrast, my blog post about the no-safe-dose rule includes example comments for the NRC, links to technical reports, and, of course, a link to the NRC site itself.[36]

If I link to this blog post on Facebook, people have everything they need in order to comment.

If the action is writing something, people like to have examples. When you ask people to write a comment to an agency, also ask them to post their comment as a comment on your blog post. That way, their comment can inspire others.

Since the website of the NRC or local commission will have many comments, having their comment clearly visible on your blog is something people can feel proud of. (Sometimes I can't even find my own comment on the big websites). This is another way people can engage with your blog, and it can be helpful to many.

If the action is a gathering or demonstration, or anything where people show up in person, your blog is a wonderful place to post pictures. Yes, you can post them on Facebook, and you should. But then what? If you want to direct people to the pictures, you have to find the URL for the Facebook album and the whole thing is a bit awkward. In general, on Facebook, people must scroll through the pictures, and that can be tedious. Most people won't look at very many of them.

Also, Facebook is by its nature totally distracting, so the pictures lose some impact.

On the other hand, your blog post can tell an illustrated story of the event, and you can link to the post directly. You can shape it so the important pictures are front and center. Your blog post can be a very powerful record of a successful action.

(Later chapters are about planning such events. This chapter is about blogs.)

And once again, we see the overlapping virtues of blog posts. Your record of the event is not only an aid to activism, it is a record on "our side" of an important event, and it is a record that aids your credibility with the mainstream press that may be covering the same event. Blogs are great!

4) Reporters may notice blogs and begin to interview you

Reporters are trying to get the story, and they use Google just as anyone else does. If your blog is covering the story, they may well read it. After they have run into your blog a certain number of times on a certain number of stories, and assuming your blog is careful and credible, you will have developed authority. Reporters may begin calling you. And if they don't, they will at least recognize you if you call them. You will have developed a platform and a reputation as a knowledgeable person. This will stand you in good stead for any activism you undertake.

5) *Blogs have staying power*

Which brings us to the fifth reason you should have a blog. Blogs have staying power. Blogs are a record of what happened, along with documents, pictures, links, comments, embedded videos, and more. When Jane is defending a power plant in the Midwest, and a tritium leak is discovered, I can send her some links to my tritium blog posts about Vermont Yankee. My posts on the subject include a wonderful guest post by a chemist: this may be very useful for Jane. Through the blog, information can be shared quickly and easily: it contains relevant information about tritium. It also (implicitly or explicitly) contains the framing information of how the controversy was addressed by pro-nuclear advocates in this area.

It is hard to overstate the importance of this. Exchange of information is key. Without it, every activist is researching and reinventing the wheel. Meanwhile, opposing activists take activist training at places like Green Camp in California.

Without the exchange of information that a blog can give you, nuclear opponents can link to slanted articles in the popular press, while nuclear supporters will have to reinvent the rebuttals. However, those rebuttals are probably already in your blog, if you have been blogging for a while!

Many times, someone will ask me about something I covered two months ago. If it were only on Facebook, I would be up a creek. It would be lost in the news stream, short, and incomplete. With a single link to my blog, I can bring that person up to speed.

In my opinion, blogs are essential.

ACTION ITEM:

Get in the loop. Find a pro-nuclear blog you like, and sign up to "follow" it, thereby getting emails about new blog posts as they are posted.

CHAPTER THIRTEEN

QUICK AND EASY BLOGGING

THERE ARE MANY BOOKS and websites and so forth about blogging. I will not attempt to duplicate these materials. Instead, here are my quick and easy blogging rules, followed by my personal-preference blogging rules.

Quick and easy rules for a good blog

- Getting started on blogging is pretty easy. I suggest that people start with the Google system, BlogSpot, because it does everything for you. Later, you may choose to move to the other major system, WordPress. I think WordPress has too many choices for a beginner. I decided to start blogging with BlogSpot as a New Year's resolution. I chose a title, ("Yes Vermont Yankee"), chose a shorter version of the title for the url (yesvy) and had my first post up within about an hour. Yes. It is that easy. And you can always change the background, the banner, the font—well, everything—later. A blog is always a work in progress.

- You will probably want to start a Twitter feed for your blog also, and maybe even a Facebook page. You can always do that later. Once you have these feeds set up, however, be sure to put up a tweet, Facebook update, LinkedIn update, Pinterest update, and everything else you might want, every time you put up a new post. If you want, you can buy entire books about doing these updates. But it's a lot easier than the books would have you believe.

- Blogging will be time consuming. When I started, I thought I had to blog every day or something. No. At this point, I try to blog every two or three days. This gives time for the posts to get some "legs'" under them (be passed around a bit by the readers) and for people to comment. Still, blogging will be time consuming. But it is worth it. You are actually creating something— an argument that explains an issue, a rebuttal to an attack on your facility—and you are creating a record. Facebook never feels that way.

- I recommend fairly short posts of less than 600 words. Alas, this is a rule I often break. Short posts are usually more readable. When you are blogging, you may have many short posts, and that's okay. At least, don't tell yourself that every post has to be long.

- Add graphics. A chart, a picture; these all make your blog more vivid and readable.

- Be honorable. Don't rip off other people's graphics. Take your own pictures or use Wikipedia pictures. Be especially careful *not* to rip off pictures taken by regular media (newspapers and magazines). They care.
- Be honorable. I am very reluctant to attack people by name. Of course, it gets a little silly if you can't name the governor. However, for most people, I use "a nuclear opponent" far more often than I use the person's name. I am not a lawyer, and this is not legal advice. It's hard to explain this simply, but basically, an attack on a private person can be seen as libel, while you can say anything you want about your senator in terms of how he is behaving as senator (or the president of a nuclear organization and how he is behaving in his role), and it is all part of the public discourse. Besides, you want to counter their arguments, not attack the person.
- Don't make it too hard for yourself to begin. Just pick your topic, marshal your arguments, and start. Afterward, you can look around at blogs you admire. Perhaps you will add some similar features to your own blog. For example, Steve Aplin's blog "Canadian Energy Issues" includes a constantly updated chart on how Ontario electricity is being generated, and the carbon content of that electricity.[37] You might want to do something like that on your blog. Rod Adams often includes a podcast as a blog post on "Atomic Insights."[38] I could make a long list of neat features, but you get the idea. *After* you get your blog started, consider which (if any) added attractions you would like to include.

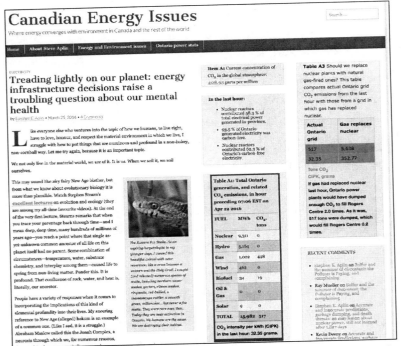

Canadian Energy Issues blog, with constantly updated carbon counter

Credit: Meredith Angwin, Steve Aplin

My blogging rule: No trolls

I HAVE ONE PERSONAL-PREFERENCE blogging rule. I don't suffer trolls.

I use my own judgment about allowing negative comments on my blog. Some bloggers allow no negative comments (some refuse to allow comments at all), and some seem to enjoy lengthy arguments with constant trolls.

This is not a free speech issue. I am a private person and my name is on my blog. I decide what appears on the blog. A study in the *Journal of Computer-Mediated Communication* and discussed on NPR shows that negative comments on a post decrease people's positive view of the main content of the post.[39]

As coauthor of the study, Dominque Brossard said, "The trolls are winning." Negative comments give people a negative view of the story.

But you don't need a research study to figure these things out. What you need to do is keep your mind clear about *why* you are doing this blog. It is to inform and encourage pro-nuclear people, and to have a record of events and answers about your local nuclear facility. Allowing trolls to run free on the blog is not helpful. And after all, they have their own blogs, do they not? Most of them have their own ways to get their ideas to the public. You should not help them.

Here's an example of why I ban trolls. I have a Facebook page called "Save Vermont Yankee." In the early days, I allowed negative comments, and boy, I sure got lots of them. At that point, I asked a question on the page: should I continue to allow negative comments? The answer was an overwhelming "no." As one person wrote (I don't have the exact words here, but basically), "I come to this page to be in a friendly place, to not be reading the Mis-Informer or hearing how terrible it is that both I and my husband work at that plant. We need this safe reading space."

Facebook is pretty good about allowing a page administrator to "Delete Comment." And the administrator can go further and "Ban User" (prevent that person from posting on that page). Since I knew the people reading my Facebook page supported me and wanted to keep the page positive, I used that power. There is similar power on a blog. I used it, and I suggest you use it also.

A final word

BASICALLY, IF YOU REMEMBER *who* you are blogging for, and follow a few simple rules of not insulting people and not ripping people off, you will have a good time blogging. What nobody tells you is that blogging becomes addictive. I write about my information about the plant . . . and people read it and comment. People whom I have never heard of—they have heard of me. It's a great deal of fun. It's also very important for my activism.

ACTION ITEM:

Begin a blog. Pretend you are going to start a new blog on BlogSpot or WordPress. Choose a template. Then, go ahead. Start the blog. Write something. Get rolling. You will be glad you did.

WHITE PAPER 3

THE BIG ACCIDENTS

HOW DEADLY IS YOUR KILOWATT? It's a big question, which I mostly addressed in White Paper 2.

But what about Chernobyl and Fukushima? How can I support nuclear power when there were such big accidents? The basic answer is that these accidents did not kill thousands and thousands of people. Many people think these accidents had huge death tolls. They didn't.

Nuclear power continues to be the least deadly form of power, kilowatt per kilowatt, even counting the accidents. Again, I refer to Conca's article on "How Deadly Is Your Kilowatt?"[40]

This white paper and its placement

INSTEAD OF INCLUDING THIS in the nuclear safety white paper (which is about ordinary operation of power plants), I put this in a separate white paper because nuclear accidents get so much press. People who hear about nuclear accidents cannot help but assume that many people died. So I felt I needed a separate white paper on the accidents.

I also decided to put this accidents white paper within the blogging section. Issues like the big accidents are another reason to have a blog. I can write a short Facebook post on many things. I can write a quick post on nuclear fuel rods versus coal ash. I can tweet about land use issues. However, it is impossible to discuss the big accidents in short form without sounding dismissive of their effects. The accidents weren't nearly as bad as they are described . . . but in a tweet, that sounds callous or dismissive of how bad they were. So, in a way, this accidents white paper is an example of the possible use of blogging.

I always want to present facts in a clear and simple way. But sometimes "simple" requires information on the background and information on comparisons. Without these, "simple" becomes a mere assertion. The consequences of the big accidents were not simple.

And with that explanation, back we go to the actual accidents white paper.

Why I still prefer nuclear power

PEOPLE ASK ME HOW I CAN like nuclear power when it has such dreadful accidents. Yes, there have been big accidents, but they have caused very little loss of life. That matters to me.

I find it hard to describe nuclear accidents to people, because I don't want to be dismissive of the effects of these accidents. However, the supposed "hundreds of thousands of deaths" or the "land is ruined forever" just isn't true.

In trying to describe the accidents, I need to distinguish between near-term deaths (acute) and predictions about future deaths (speculative deaths). Sometimes these distinctions are called "deterministic" consequences and "stochastic" consequences. However, many of the predictions about nuclear accidents do not deserve the technical term "stochastic." So I will continue to use the words "predicted" and "speculative."

Also, the land is ruined forever? Again, not to be dismissive, but people are moving back, quite safely, within five to thirty years of the accident. This is not the same as saying, "nothing happened." But it is also not the same as saying, "nobody will ever live there again."

Forest fire analogy

TO EXPLAIN PART OF THE REASON I support nuclear energy despite the accidents, I came up with an analogy to forest fires. Let's say there is a forest fire. Let's say two people do not evacuate their home when it was suggested they do so. They die. Let's say the fire makes a great deal of smoke, and a nearby city is blanketed with smoke for several days. Smoke is not good for the lungs, and people will be urged to stay inside.

How will this fire be described? The news reports will say that "two people died." That is, the acute effect of the fire will be announced. The fire may well have long-term health effects. These are unlikely to be announced, because they are so tenuous and hard to calculate. Future effects that are small, hard to measure, and basically speculative are not announced for fires and other accidents. No radio station will broadcast, "Increase in lung cancer expected in this city, due to two days of exposure to forest fire smoke."

Except, of course, the way nuclear accidents are described. For nuclear accidents, speculations of future harm supply frightening articles, radio shows, TV shows, and so forth. Every nuclear accident is described as one step away from the complete death of humans on the planet, as described in Nevil Shute's novel *On the Beach*.

Such speculations on future effects are generally not announced for other technologies. Therefore, it is completely understandable that most people confuse speculative, future, uncertain effects for nuclear accidents with a right-now casualty list.

For myself, I have tried to separate this out, because I want to be able to talk to people about the accidents without being dismissive of people's fears. It's not easy.

What we know about the accidents

SO I HAD TO FIGURE OUT about those future deaths. Does anybody know how many future deaths are likely to occur?

Actually, we do know, in a general way. The United Nations and World Health Organization have been following these accidents for years, trying to understand their health effects.

Their conclusions are that there are almost no future health effects to be expected from accident radiation. Any effects will be mostly impossible to distinguish from health effects from other causes. Similarly, long-term health effects from the effects of a forest fire smoke would be hard to distinguish from effects from other causes.

Scientists and doctors concerned with public health do many studies to understand the causes of disease. For example, it has long been noticed that bladder cancer rates are higher than expected in the Northeast. Only recently, the cause has been determined: arsenic in well water.[41]

In contrast, the nuclear accidents have not led to increased cancer rates, except in first responders at Chernobyl. However, that statement can seem dismissive of these accidents. So I need to look at the accidents in greater detail.

Here is my personal understanding of the Big Three Accidents.

Three Mile Island

- No acute deaths.
- Land use: some voluntary evacuation (most people stayed). People returned within three weeks.
- Sister plants: TMI-2 accident was in 1979; TMI-1 continues to operate.
- Predicted deaths: none, according to the most careful US report: BEIR II. The US BEIR report ("Biological Effects of Ionizing Radiation") states that "[t]he collective dose equivalent resulting from the radioactivity released in the Three Mile Island accident was so low that the estimated number of excess cancer cases to be expected, if any were to occur, would be negligible and undetectable."[42]
- Speculative deaths: nuclear opponents expect huge numbers and are eager to seize upon any report that shows any increase in the death rate in any nearby area among any group.

Chernobyl

THE CHERNOBYL ACCIDENT was the result of a flawed reactor design that was operated by inadequately trained personnel. The reactor did not even have containment.

Acute health effects: thirty people died from acute radiation sickness.[43]

Evacuation: widespread. Over 300,000 people evacuated. History of the zones is quite complex, but more than 1,000 square miles were evacuated.[44]

Wildlife is now flourishing in the evacuated areas. In fact, in 2011 Chernobyl was officially declared a tourist attraction.[45]

As usual in evacuations, people are beginning to move back, and areas of "exclusion" are being lifted. This is a complex story. The World Nuclear Association fact sheet gives some of the history. Read "Resettlement of Contaminated Areas."[46]

Sister plants: The Reactor 4 accident was in 1986. Reactor 3 at Chernobyl continued to produce power until 2000.

People usually think the entire Chernobyl area became a completely dead zone that nobody could enter. Actually, people continued to work in the neighboring plants. These workers undoubtedly had dosimeters and were monitored. I expect they will stay in good health, as do most nuclear workers.[47]

Predicted deaths: Best data I can find: up to 4,000 deaths from cancer.

UNSCEAR forum concludes about Chernobyl:

Although those exposed as children and the emergency and recovery workers are at increased risk of radiation-induced effects, the vast majority of the population need not live in fear of serious health consequences due to the radiation from the Chernobyl accident . . .

There was a "dramatic increase" in thyroid cancers from Chernobyl (approximately 6,000 more cancers), but there is no clearly demonstrated increase in other cancers in the exposed population. Survival rates for thyroid cancers is almost 99 percent.[48, 49]

The World Nuclear Organization fact sheet gives an excellent overview of the history.[50]

Speculative deaths: Oh, of course you know. Opponents expect not several thousand cancers, as predicted by the UN, but hundreds of thousands of deaths. Millions even. When estimating deaths from Chernobyl, the sky is always the limit.

Chernobyl was the worst nuclear accident in history. I think that it will always be the worst nuclear accident in history. They truly "do not build them like that anymore." Not even in Russia.

Fukushima

THE EARTHQUAKE AND TSUNAMI that struck Japan was a tragic natural disaster, which caused 19,000 deaths. However, these deaths were not caused by the nuclear plants. Let's look at the Fukushima plants, instead.

Direct deaths: Three TEPCO employees were killed at Fukushima as a result of the earthquake or tsunami. There have been no deaths or cases of radiation sickness from the nuclear accident. Three workers received "beta burns" and were briefly hospitalized.[51]

Evacuation: More than 100,000 people were evacuated, and official figures show that there have been well over 1,000 deaths from the evacuation. Evacuations were done in a panicked and hurried manner, and older people who could not live without warmth and medicines were in a situation where they had neither. Government nervousness has also delayed the return of many people to their homes.[52]

Other reports show the number of evacuation deaths to be above 2,900.[53]

Sister Plants: Fukushima Daiichi units 1, 2, 3, 4 were severely affected by the tsunami. However, several nearby plants were shut down effectively. None of these plants are operating now, some due to tsunami damage, others due to Japanese government policy.

Several other units shut down successfully: Fukushima Daiichi units 5 and 6, in the same complex as units 1 through 4, and Fukushima Daiini, a 3-unit plant seven miles away from Daiichi. With quick action, all these units utilized their limited electricity supplies effectively.[54, 55]

The Onagawa plant (units 1, 2, 3) was closer to the epicenter, but was basically undamaged, and served as a refuge for about 300 people whose homes were washed away by the tsunami.[56]

The radiation released at Fukushima would not have caused any acute (immediate) deaths or sickness. The massive evacuation was expected to prevent future deaths, and the number of the future deaths was always speculative.

The Japanese government ordered evacuations within a radius 20 km around the plant, and encouraged voluntary evacuations in areas up to 30 km around the plant. One problem with this massive evacuation is that it becomes difficult to lift the orders and expect people to return home. People are returning home, however.

To keep up with the ongoing resettlement of the Fukushima area, and the reactor clean-up, I recommend Leslie Corrice's excellent blog "Fukushima Accident Updates."[57]

Predicted deaths: According to the best data I can find, there will be some possible deaths from thyroid cancer. Other cancer rates will not increase measurably above baseline.

The World Health Organization did a major study of the health effects of the Fukushima meltdown. In 2013, they published a health risk assessment from the nuclear accident after the 2011 Great East Japan Earthquake and Tsunami.[58]

As they wrote in the executive summary of the report (links to report and summary included in press release above): *Outside the geographical areas most affected by radiation, even in locations within Fukushima prefecture, the predicted risks remain low and no observable increases in cancer above natural variation in baseline rates are anticipated.*

Meanwhile, within those areas most affected by radiation from releases at Fukushima, some cancer increases are predicted. Particularly, thyroid cancer increases are expected for people who were exposed as infants. As WHO notes in the executive summary: *The additional lifetime risk estimated (for thyroid cancer) in this assessment for a female infant exposed in the most affected location is one-half of one percent.* This increased rate may be detectable, and people in the area should have thyroid screenings for this largely curable cancer.

Speculative deaths: Immense, of course. Millions. The entire Pacific totally contaminated. Et cetera. One opponent suggested that people should evacuate the northern hemisphere, if the fuel pool at reactor four collapsed. Yes, I can't make this stuff up.

Accidents, nuclear safety and me

WHY DO I STILL SUPPORT NUCLEAR, despite these accidents? Basically, because very few people died, and very few people will die.

With nuclear accidents, the press treats future possibilities as current certainties. This is completely misleading. If you count immediate deaths (forest fire analogy), there are about 40 at Chernobyl. For all the accidents, "future deaths" from cancer are so few that it is unclear that any such deaths will be detected among other causes of cancer in the population (except for thyroid cancer at Chernobyl and possibly at Fukushima). Considering how coal and gas and oil lead to real-time casualties, nuclear remains the safest form of electricity production. That is one of the reasons I like it.

In terms of the land, people are resettling both Chernobyl and Fukushima. I think the evacuation zones for both areas were far too big, and based on a far too alarmist view of the effect of radiation on future cancers. However, this is not a research project, so I am not going to argue "how big should the zone have been" in this book. Still, when you get right down to it, the nuclear plants next to Chernobyl kept operating. People worked at those plants. People are moving back to the affected zones of both Chernobyl and Fukushima within five to twenty years after the accidents. The permanently dead, no-go areas, ruined forever . . . is basically an imaginary scenario built on fear. It has little to do with the facts on the ground.

In Fukushima especially, the evacuations killed people, and the accident would not have killed them. The real problem was the culture of fear surrounding radiation.

To understand the "culture of fear" that led to ill-thought-out and dangerous evacuations at Fukushima, I recommend Wade Allison's book, *Radiation and Reason.*[59]

I also recommend Robert Hargraves' talk about radiation safety.[60]

Being killed by fossil fuels is far more likely than being killed by nuclear energy. That matters to me.

Safety matters.

Blogging

AND, IN WHAT MIGHT BE CONSIDERED a lame attempt at a transition, I believe that having a blog matters to the activist.

Sometimes, you have to write more than a tweet to cover the bases. Sometimes the situation is complicated and needs lots of links.

Sometimes, only a blog post can honor, describe, and comment upon a situation.

CHAPTER FOURTEEN

ABOUT WRITING FOR THE WEB

(Mostly About Blogging)

PEOPLE READ DIFFERENTLY on the web. Shorter paragraphs and shorter sentences are easier on the eyes. The same person who will cheerfully tackle a long dense article in *The New Yorker* will rebel against reading a blog post that presents itself as a solid mass of gray text. It is different, reading on the web.

Even for print media, printers knew, long ago, that people need a break in reading. That is why they inserted these little printer's decorations.

Similarly, fiction writers use dialog for various purposes. One purpose of dialog is to break up the text and make it more readable.

You have to do this sort of thing, and more, for web reading. A technical writing course that I took on "writing for the web" stressed that we should make liberal use of white space, use lots of bullets, break up the text, use sub-headings, and use short sentences. Apparently, it is physically harder to read steadily, online. Luckily, unlike a print book, on the web you don't pay any extra paper costs when you insert some white space.

Graphic design and pictures

ALSO, THE IDEA THAT GROWNUPS don't like pictures . . . just isn't true. There used to be color prints in children's books but not in grownups' books for cost reasons. In the old days, color printing was time consuming to set up and costly to print. But your blog isn't an old-fashioned book. It's on the web. There's no cost for printing in color, and Wikipedia pictures and your own pictures are free to use.

Yes Vermont Yankee
A blog about Northeast energy issues, and in support of nuclear power.

WEDNESDAY, MAY 25, 2011

Nimby and Nukes: Vermont Utility Makes a Deal with Seabrook

The Deal

Yesterday Green Mountain Power (GMP) announced a deal to buy electricity from Seabrook Station in New Hampshire. The deal was at a very good price, 4.66 cents per kWh, less than Vermont Yankee's recent offer price of 4.9 cents, and far less than the 5.8 cents from Hydro-Quebec that led to general rejoicing earlier this year.

The amount of power purchased from Seabrook varies between 15 and 60 MW from year to year. In 2012, GMP will buy 15 MW of power from Seabrook. This amount goes up to 60 MW in 2015. According to the article, GMP now buys 100 MW from Vermont Yankee. (GMP and Central Vermont Public Service share most of the approximately 200 MW that Vermont Yankee supplies to Vermont.)

Blog post with picture of Seabrook nuclear plant, as memory aid.

Pictures not only break up the text, but they also act as a memory aid. "Oh yeah, that blog post . . . it had a picture of a storm cloud, as I recall, yeah, here it is!" For example, I have a post called "Nimby and Nukes" about Vermont utilities buying power from Seabrook but not from Vermont Yankee.[61] In this post, I have a picture of Seabrook, courtesy of Wikipedia.

Many WordPress themes have a "featured image" choice for similar reasons. I use Google BlogSpot, and I almost always put an image on the upper left corner of my blog post.

Beyond pictures, you need to choose a graphic design. Luckily, you don't have to be a graphic designer in order have a pleasant and readable blog. Most blogging platforms have excellent choices of templates, in which the colors and the fonts and . . . well . . . everything makes a pleasing whole. (The blogging platforms have hired the graphic designers; you don't have to. You just choose the theme or template you like best.)

But you are responsible for making the blog contents themselves readable. For readability, you need to semi-graphic-design your actual blog contents. Yes. Design the words.

Readability for the words on your blog

- Short sentences, or at least short paragraphs.
- No dense masses of text.
- Use white space to break things up.
- Use graphics, both to head each blog post and to break up text.
- Don't use reverse text (white letters on a black background, for example). It's hard to read.

These few tricks will make your blog post far more readable.

ACTION ITEM:

Model another site. Look at a good commercial site on the web. Notice how much white space they have, and notice the illustrations. If you like it, bookmark it as a possible model for your blog.

CHAPTER FIFTEEN

THE ACTIVIST'S EMAIL LIST

IN CHAPTER 3 we discussed collecting names and contact information of pro-nuclear people you meet. In this chapter, we'll discuss ways to organize that information into an email list and how to use it.

There are books and websites and courses and seminars and teleseminars and podcasts—all about growing your email list. I'm only going to write a chapter on it. Where shall I start?

Email lists are essential

ALL THOSE BOOKS AND WEBSITES exist because email is an important subject, and it is not an easy one to tackle in a single chapter. In contrast, a blog can be started at midnight on New Year's Eve. "It's my resolution, and I'm doing it before this champagne-courage wears off." That is how I started my blog. Starting a blog is not a big deal.

In contrast to blogging, getting an email list together is important, essential, and *hard*. In short, it may be worthwhile to buy some of those books or go to some of those seminars. Grow your list.

Once again, I have advice, and I think it is good advice. However (unlike some of the other chapters), I don't think I have enough advice. Your email list is golden. Your email list is the way you can notify people to take action. Furthermore, unlike your blog or your Facebook page, you can get clear feedback on which parts of your list work and which parts of your list don't work.

Why we need a list

BASICALLY, AS ACTIVISTS WE HAVE email lists in order to encourage and help people support the plant or other local nuclear facility. The people who have agreed to be on your email list are people who are willing to get emails. They are more strongly self-selected than your Facebook followers or your blog followers. The ones on your email list will send comments to the Public Service Board, show up for a demonstration, and donate to your cause (if you have set it up for donations). They will be the stalwarts and the volunteers.

Let's start at the beginning.

What is the list?

YOU HAVE FOUND SOME PRO-NUCLEAR people to add to your list, but what do you do with them once you've found them?

First of all, you need to define what information will be on the email list. There are three things you must have on the list:

- The person's name

- The person's email address
- Where you met them

Also, it is very nice to have (and people usually don't mind sharing this):

- The town and state they live in

The reason I want to know town and state is that for some things, it is important to be a Vermont resident. If there is a hearing in Montpelier, it is good to know who lives near Montpelier and can easily get to Montpelier. If something is going to happen in Massachusetts that affects Vermont, it is good to be able to generate a smaller email list of "people from Massachusetts."

I don't ask for phone numbers, but if I am growing my list and someone says, "Sure, here's my card," I won't throw away the information about that person's address, company, phone number, etc.

Finding the people

AS WE DISCUSSED IN CHAPTER 3, you should meet pro-nuclear people and grow your contact list every chance you get. There's an old saying about sales: "Always be closing." Well, for activism, a similar mantra is important: "Always be recruiting."

You should recruit, if possible, three ways:

1. In person
2. Through websites and social media
3. By sharing lists with related organizations.

Recruiting in person

THIS IS THE EASIEST and the hardest.

It is easiest because all you have to do is hand around a sign-up sheet at meetings. You gave a talk: start it with asking people to add their names to the sign-up sheet if they want more information. The top of the sign-up sheet should have the date and the name of the event. You need to know where you met these people. The sheet should have space for name, email address, and town and state. Hopefully, you have a friend with you because, trust me, people have terrible handwriting and many of the email addresses will be just borderline legible. You will not be able to recapture this information, so have your friend look over the sign-up sheet and wander around, asking people to clear up the ambiguities.

You can also accept business cards from people. You can trade cards with people. There are many ways to recruit in person.

I think it is easiest to recruit in person. But I acknowledge that you are standing near someone and asking for something—and this is never easy.

However, remember that you are actually *offering* something: information. If they are interested, they will have a reviewed and curated source of information on a subject that they want to know more about. *You* will be putting in time deciding what to send, what to ask for, what links to include in your requests, etc. You will be providing a service.

I always tell people that I plan to send emails about twice a month: they will not get spammed. Of course, with breaking news, they might get an occasional extra email. People are usually quite happy with this. Also, the email service has a clear opt-out mechanism, and so they can drop at any time, without being forced to interact with a person. Just drop—easy.

Once you begin to realize that you are offering a service, you will feel better about asking for people's names. You need to remind yourself that you are doing this for the good of the planet. Also, remember that the people on your list are busy. They cannot easily get the information that you offer.

Recruiting through the web

THIS GETS MORE COMPLEX. The simple way is equivalent to recruiting in person: if someone is commenting on your blog or sharing your Facebook posts, send that person a message asking them to send you their email address for your mailing list. Explain what your list is and why they would want to join it. You can do this through the comment section of your blog or through Facebook messaging. Put your own email address out there for them to respond, but don't write it as mjangwin@ gmail.com because a malicious bot could pick that up and spam you. I always write mjangwin at gmail.

You can also use a blog post to ask people to join your email list. Same with a Facebook post.

Sharing lists with related organizations

OKAY. LET'S BE BLUNT. Your list is sacred to you, and you told the people on the list you would never share it. And guess what? Most organizations feel the same about their own lists.

That means that you can't trade lists with another organization (usually) and then both of you suddenly have bigger email lists.

However, you can trade emails. If you have a good relationship (both personal and in some shared goals) with an organization, you can write an email and ask that organization to send it to their list. Your email will have information about what you are doing, and it will include an email address where they can opt-in. Meanwhile, you will send an email from that organization to your email list, and people on your list can opt-in to their list.

Frankly, I am including this only for completeness. Organizations guard their email lists, and this kind of swap is hard to set up. But you might be able to do it with a local group sympathetic to your cause. For example, you might be able to do arrange this sort of email exchange with a local ANS section or a union active at the plant, etc.

Always be recruiting

GROWING AN EMAIL LIST is slow work. You can get hints from this chapter and from many books. The important thing is:

Always be recruiting (to your email list).

This is the equivalent of the sales mantra: "Always be closing!"

For activists, it is:

Always be recruiting.

By having this list, you give people who support nuclear energy a way to show their support. You will send emails, and the people who receive these emails will learn about controversies and about opportunities for support. In other words, this list is not just some kind of ego trip.

It is part of your way to serve the nuclear community and the bigger community of the planet.

Not just one list

AS YOU MAY HAVE GUESSED by now, there is not just One List. I mean, there is one list, and my list of almost 1,000 people is my "Big List." But the Big List is far more useful if it is subdivided.

My Big List is divided into:

- People I met at ANS meetings
- People I met at energy meetings
- People I met at political meetings (Republican)
- People I met at political meetings (Democrat)
- People I met "various places" (Constant Contact even has a category for this: "not classified elsewhere")
- People who gave my group some money
- People I met at Rotary Clubs
- People who joined via the web
- People in the media

Using the list: The mail service

OH DEAR. NOW I have to tell you the bad news.

You need a mail service. You simply cannot organize and keep track of this many people on your own computer (I've tried). Here's why:

First off, you need to send emails bcc (blind copy). You need to send bcc because you don't want your list public, for two reasons.

- For the sake of the people who don't want to be visible as public supporters of nuclear energy. After all, many people give money to charities as "anonymous." And I am talking about money to well-accepted charities like the local art museum, not something as possibly divisive as "a supporter of nuclear power."
- For your own sake. Your list is valuable and it took time and effort to grow it. Sending it in the open is an invitation to stealing the list. Then, when people on the list get tons of emails from people they never heard of . . . who are they going to blame? You, of course.

The bad news is that most computer mail programs won't let you send an email with with more than twenty bcc. The people who set up the programs don't want people using the mail program service to send spam.

Before I got a mail service, I had something like thirty lists, each of which had less than twenty emails on the list (so I could send to them bcc). It was hard to keep those lists well-classified (where I met the people, for example). Sometimes people asked to drop their name off the list, and I didn't get around to it (or I did get around to it, but I had mistakenly put their name on two lists and dropped it only from one list). Then they quite rightly got mad at me. Sometimes I sent to the same list twice and so forth.

And I never knew who opened the mail and who didn't. I not only wasted time, I lost information.

A service like Mailchimp or Constant Contact will send to the specific sub-lists you want to send to (for example, to Democrats, or to people who have donated money). You will see who opened the mail and who didn't. If you discover that people you meet at Rotary Clubs open your mail regularly, and people you meet at Republican clubs open it rarely, you know that to get more helpful activists you should spend more time at Rotaries.

The main email services are Mailchimp and Constant Contact.[62] Mailchimp is free up to a certain number of email addresses, and Constant Contact costs money. Evaluate your own situation, but *do* use a service. Don't drive yourself as nuts as I drove myself when I had thirty lists, complete with overlaps (which the service will check for you). I was also completely unable to know what kind of groups were most likely to yield people who opened the mail and wanted to be advocates.

ACTION ITEM:

Use your email list. You've been creating an email list, now use it to create a small "call to action" email request. This can be as simple as sharing a biased or anti-nuclear letter to the editor, providing factual points to dispute the letter, and asking your email list to send letters refuting the original letter. (You can do the same with an online article.)

CHAPTER SIXTEEN

RAISING MONEY

ONCE YOU HAVE A mailing list, you can use it to raise money. That's the theory, anyway.

However, you are not just selling popcorn or candy bars or books or theater tickets. You want to raise money for nuclear advocacy.

Or maybe you don't.

This book is about nuclear advocacy, and so we will discuss the issues that are unique to being a nuclear advocate. Many of these issues are internal: How do you feel? What do you want to do? As they say on Facebook about some relationships, "It's complicated." Once you understand your own feelings, your choices will be clearer.

Let's start at the top and continue to the methods. Most books on raising money take the top issues for granted and get right down to the nitty-gritty of bringing the dollars in the door. We will spend comparatively little time on "bringing the dollars in." As a nuclear advocate, you must tackle the advocacy issues first.

Why raise money?

SOME PEOPLE DON'T WANT TO raise money. They prefer to be self-funded. One sincere nuclear advocate wrote on Facebook that he didn't think we should get involved with starting a 501c3 (educational and charitable organization) or, indeed, do anything that raises money in a visible way. Oddly, he suggested that if advocates needed money, they should raise it like "the Boy Scouts do." Perhaps he is unaware that the Boy Scouts are a 501c3 organization with a "donate" page on their main website.[63]

The problem is that raising money can be an uncomfortable activity for a pro-nuclear advocate. There's the fear of being called a shill. It's a real fear, and you *will* be called a shill. My opinion is, don't worry about it. You will be called a shill even if you don't get a penny from anyone. I certainly was, as soon as I started my blog, despite the fact I didn't get nothing from nobody, and I didn't even have a donate button on the blog.

Rod Adams, the publisher of *Atomic Insights*, has advice for people who avoid asking for money for fear of being called names: "Money is a tool that helps you perform tasks. Nuclear energy opponents understand that. When they fling accusations, their intent is to cause nuclear advocates to unilaterally disarm. They have no problem accepting money that helps them achieve their goals, but they would prefer to do battle with individuals operating on a shoestring budget."

Let's look at why you might want to raise money. If you use the money from your own pocket, you will find yourself not doing things that could be very helpful to your work. You will decide that the meeting is too far away, and you can't afford the hotel room for the night. It took me forever to decide on using a paid email service. An email service is essential, but Constant Contact costs me money every month. (You can choose Mailchimp, however, which offers a free "starter" package.)

Reasons you need money

WHY RAISE MONEY:

1. Not your own pocket

   Unless you are quite wealthy, self-funding becomes limited. It is limited in two ways: the amount of actual money you can expend, and the pushback you may get from your family. You *will* be spending money, if only on travel to meeting sites (mileage or possibly airfares); some blogging platforms cost money each month, and if you have a non-blogging website you will have to buy a domain name and a hosting service and maybe software. You can be a very low-cost nuclear advocate, but it isn't free.

2. Opportunity costs

   And this doesn't even count the opportunity cost issue. In the beginning, I was also seeking technical writing contracts to make some money, but later I didn't have time. I was in a writing group online with some other people, three of whom now have multiple book contracts for an entire mystery series. I didn't have time to keep submitting my novels to agents, so no money coming in there.

Meanwhile, a friend of mine laments the time he should have been spending on home upkeep. Now, as he hires contractors to do what he feels he neglected earlier, the costs of advocacy are coming home to him.

The root word of "decision" comes from the Latin for "cut" or "separate." You have cut out other choices by spending your time being a nuclear advocate. And many of those other choices would have saved you money or made money for you.

3. Pushback from your family
   Many of us have experienced this. Even if we are more or less comfortably retired, nuclear advocacy can be an expensive "hobby." Self-funding advocacy can begin to feel weird.

4. No money
   You will not do things you want to do and even need to do, because you don't have money to do them.

5. Age segregation
   Without money, most of the people in your group will be retirees. Your demographic of fellow advocates can become very narrow. This just plays into the anti-nuclear accusations about the kind of people who support nuclear energy.

6. No young people
   Young people need some money to participate. Not a lot: this can be seen as building their resume, but they

need some. The opponent organizations load themselves up with interns, and these interns get a lot done.

7. Interns

My energy education project had two interns. They did amazing things for the projects, and they learned a great deal about nuclear energy and became even more favorable toward it. (Obviously, I would not have asked nuclear opponents to be interns. However, young people, even if they are eager to be pro-nuclear interns, may not know much about nuclear energy.)

The ability to hire interns is a *very* important part of why you should raise money. One of the anti-nuclear organizations blankets Vermont with bicycle-riding interns in the summer. They go to every house with their surveys and handouts. We can't hope to have that many interns, but we need some, or it will be a lonely job being pro-nuclear.

Also, those young people who blanket Vermont on their bicycles each summer, spreading their anti-nuclear message and getting paid for it . . . they will be anti-nuclear for life, I expect. Pro-nuclear groups need to have at least some interns to keep nuclear in the running for the future.

I hope I have convinced you of the usefulness of raising money. If this were any subject except pro-nuclear advocacy, the usefulness of money would be a given! But in nuclear advocacy, the fear of "being a shill" is so heavy that you will meet people who refuse to do anything except be self-funded. I hope I have convinced you that being self-funded is the wrong path.

Now that you decided to raise money

As I SAID, most money-raising information (books, websites) starts with the idea that "of course you have to raise money." It's a given.

I hope I have convinced you that you should, indeed, raise money. So now we can go on to the question, "Where can you get money?" Now, the latter question is generally answered only in practical terms. For pro-nuclear advocates, however, there are yet more questions.

First, a word about my opinion on this. I think that, just as many nuclear opponents are overly frightened of radiation, nuclear proponents are overly frightened of the word "shill." One of my friends, when asked how much she gets from the nuclear industry for supporting them, replies, "Oh no. I am so dumb that I do it for free." That works well for her, but my own experience is that you are going to be called a shill anyway, so just move forward and raise money. Okay, enough opinions.

The internal game of raising money

THE FIRST PART IS TO confront your internal game. Your feelings. Being an activist is not the equivalent of selling services. Big companies hire public relations companies, and these companies do . . . well, whatever they do. But the important thing is that PR companies get paid for what they do, for their service to their client. If the client stops paying them, they stop working for that client. It's a pretty simple model for a transaction.

Frankly, for most of us, this is an emotionally safe model. You pay me, and I will do something that will benefit you. It's a sale. We can all feel good about selling something.

As an activist, though, you have to have a different model. You will do Good Things for the world, and you will ask people for money to help you do these things. Of course this is the way nonprofits generally function, so no big deal, right?

The fear of the begging letter

AND MEANWHILE, WE GET LETTERS from the charities that we usually give money to. My husband hands the envelopes to me with the brief comment, "Some more begging letters today." So, one thing that stands in everyone's way when seeking funding for a not-for-profit, or anytime you seek funding and don't return a direct service in return, is the feeling of begging.

Sometimes I think it would be easier to be a hitman than a not-for-profit. After all, while the service provided is cruel, illegal, and immoral . . . it is a service. The hitman knows exactly the task he has to perform in order to get paid. I sometimes feel as if it is equally immoral to ask for money for my not-for-profit. After all, I am not going to do *anything* for the person who gave me the money.

I am not going to say, "You have to get over this." This is not easy to "get over." Presidents of long-lasting not-for-profits and college professors applying for grants have all told me: I HATE fundraising.

This is one of those situations where you must keep in mind why you are a nuclear activist. Also, remember that most people who do fundraising, even for causes to which they have dedicated most of their lives . . . don't like to do fundraising.

Move from "why" to "how" as soon as possible

MY ADVICE, BEYOND THE usual "know thyself," is to work with someone you know who is a fundraiser or development director or whatever that person is called in the not-for-profit. The secret (such as it is) is to get beyond the "Oh should I do this, why should anyone give my group any money?" etc., etc. spinning in your head, and get right down to "*How* do we do this?" Working with a professional fundraiser can teach you more, partially from the interactions with a real person, than any words I can write on this page.

Can I ask for money from the industry?

OKAY. YOU HAVE SQUASHED the demons of "How can I ask for money?" These are the universal demons. And now you are right up against the nuclear proponent demons.

Whom do I ask? And most importantly, should I ask for money from nuclear plants? I have said before that I don't believe you are a shill if you ask for money from nuclear plants. After all, they didn't come up to you and bribe you: "Please, I know you hate us, but please take our money and change your mind!" No, you are pro-nuclear and you are seeking money. The nuclear companies are not seeking you, like the Devil in some kind of morality play, trying to get ahold of your soul.

On the other hand, some people refuse to take any money from the nuclear industry in order to solidify their position as being totally independent of the industry. This is also a valid stance.

Clearly, you have to make your own decision on this.

Being a not-for-profit . . . or not being a not-for-profit

THE CLEANEST WAY TO BE a not-for-profit is to start your own. With your own not-for-profit, *you* completely define the mission statement. However, starting your own not-for-profit means filing forms with the government, having a board of directors, keeping minutes, and filing tax returns (if you receive more than $10,000 per year).

I tend to be paperwork-averse because there are so many other things to do with a cheerful afternoon. Luckily for me, I found that the Ethan Allen Institute founder, John McClaughry, was a former nuclear engineer, and my work became the "Energy Education Project" of the Ethan Allen Institute. While I still had to raise funds, the funds were donated to the Institute, not to me, and the Institute kept track of them. This was very helpful.

The Ethan Allen Institute is a free-market think tank, which is okay with me. The Ethan Allen Institute doesn't take stands on social issues, such as gay marriage. Nevertheless, I began to feel awkward sometimes because Democrats automatically lumped me with "them": the Republicans, the Tea Party, whatever. If I had started my own not-for-profit, which was all about energy and not about free markets, I might have had a bigger reach with speaking engagements. I have never been invited to speak before a Democratic group.

There were definitely problems with my avoidance of hassle and paperwork. On the other hand, the people at the Ethan Allen Institute were always thoughtful and supportive and willing to talk with me. That is also an advantage of joining an existing not-for-profit.

On the other hand, the days of having to become a not-for-profit may be over. Web-based organizations, such as KickStarter, GoFundMe, and Indiegogo, do not require corporate person-hood. The documentary *Once Upon a Nuclear Ship . . . the NS Savannah Documentary*[64] was partially funded through Indiegogo. You owe it to yourself to explore your options.

How to raise money for a not-for-profit

THERE ARE BOOKS AND WEBSITES GALORE on this topic, as you can imagine. I recommend you read some of them, and at least subscribe to the free email updates from Guidestar. You may want to buy a subscription to this service. It is full of good advice, plus nitty-gritty details on where the grants are right now.[65]

There are basically five sources of funding:

- Businesses
- Foundations
- Grants
- Donations from people
- Memberships

As I mentioned above, your best bet is to talk to someone who is familiar with the fundraising process. This is simply too big to cover in a part of a chapter.

Money and intervenors

SOME STATES HAVE FUNDING for groups that "intervene" in various public hearings. The idea behind state funding is that big organizations can hire lawyers, but citizens' groups with limited funds have a hard time combatting the big boys. The state intervenor funds are supposed to level the playing field between the corporations and the citizenry.

As you can imagine, anti-nuclear groups are often recipients of state intervenor money. I have heard of grants in the six figures to anti-nuclear groups. However, the rules are not written as "this money is for anti-nuclear groups." All groups have to prove they meet the criteria to be intervenors. If you live in a state that disburses intervenor's funds, you owe it to yourself to learn the state's "intervenor" rules and obtain state "intervenor" money. Or, at least, attempt to obtain it. You won't get any money if you don't try.

You decide to self-fund

AFTER ALL THESE CAVEATS and all these choices, you may have decided to self-fund after all. Let me stress that you don't have to do everything and certainly don't have to do everything at once.

To run a program, about one-third of your time will be spent on fundraising. But you may decide you just want to run a mini-program, and you can spend a tenth of your time on fundraising. Maybe your entire program consists of a mileage allowance for yourself and payment for a summer intern. In that case, you may be able to raise a few thousand dollars each year from an angel donor who supports your cause. Any level of money you raise is basically okay.

I just hate it when people don't attempt to raise money at all. Unless you are rich, I think that completely self-funding is a mistake. It's like fighting with one hand tied behind your back.

ACTION ITEM:

Think budgeting. Think of three things you would do if you had $10,000 to spend on increasing your advocacy. Write them down. Are these things worth going to the trouble of fundraising?

CHAPTER SEVENTEEN

WHEN IT DOESN'T FEEL LIKE ENOUGH

But it isn't enough!

I HAVE TO ADDRESS THIS problem right here, and keep addressing it. Whatever you do, it is never enough. It never feels like enough. Success is never complete. Activism brings an emotional backlash for the activist.

To some extent, this is my problem too. I finish something and feel good about it . . . and then I think of all the other things I "should" do and about all the opponents who will belittle what I "did" do, and it can be miserable.

This feeling goes with the territory of trying to make a difference. Mother Teresa fought despair and depression. Isaac Newton felt as if he had been standing on a seashore, picking up pebbles, while the ocean of truth lay undiscovered before him. I suspect that Thomas Jefferson, Martin Luther King Jr., Jonas Salk, and every person involved in a discovery or political movement that meant something to the person—felt the same way.

> I was like a boy playing on the sea-shore, and diverting myself now and then finding a smoother pebble or a prettier shell than ordinary, whilst the great ocean of truth lay undiscovered before me.
>
> —ISAAC NEWTON[66]

My advice is to just be mindful of the feeling (oh yes, that despair thing again), accept that you feel it, and go on.

Two things that help me are my friend Howard Shaffer's frequent remarks about "the wit of the staircase." This is a description of what happens when a comment renders you speechless. You are actually speechless. You only think of a witty response when you have left the conversation, left the room, and reached the bottom of the staircase.[67] It helps me to remember that this happens to everybody.

Another thing that helps me is the Jewish statement in the Pirkei Avot: "It is not incumbent upon you to complete the work, but neither are you at liberty to desist from it."[68]

People must take whatever action they can take, or use whatever skills they have, to repair the world. Everyone must take action, but nobody is going to "complete the work" of making this a better world. And nobody is going to take action perfectly. Nobody always has the right response.

For me, I guess this comes back to the incremental-improvement idea that led me to become a chemist, not a physicist.

As an activist, I move the needle of public discourse toward support for nuclear energy. I make a contribution toward the happiness and energy security of the world.

The despair thing is different from disappointment or sorrow. I feel great sorrow about Vermont Yankee closing. For me, sorrow is a dark, sad pervasive feeling—but it isn't despair. The "despair"' thing is about futility, the idea I could have done my work much better, that my work is useless.

This feeling becomes a companion to all those who work hard to make a difference. However, the feeling is not a constant companion.

"It is not incumbent upon you to complete the work, but neither are you at liberty to desist from it."

Joy Everett and James MacBride. At the rally in front of the Brattleboro Courthouse, September 12, 2011.

ACTION ITEM:

Your reasons. Write down the reasons you are a nuclear advocate, or why you consider nuclear power to be an essential technology for the future.

Print these statements and put them on your bulletin board. Or frame them and mount them on your wall. Or just prop them up on your desk where you can see them. These statements will remind you why you are an activist. Meanwhile, remind yourself that you are . . . moving the needle.

CHAPTER EIGHTEEN

INTERMEZZO

How far that little candle throws his beams!
So shines a good deed in a naughty world.
—PORTIA, MERCHANT OF VENICE, SHAKESPEARE

Mary Freeman

MARY FREEMAN'S DAUGHTER was happy in her new gymnastics class, and Mary adapted very quickly to the driving schedule. It was a shame she had to drive her daughter twenty miles to a class when there was a perfectly fine gymnastics program within walking distance of her school. But it was too miserable, with some of the other girls harassing her because her father worked at the nuclear plant, and the teacher basically taking their side.

Well, one nice thing about driving is that sometimes she and her daughter spoke more in the car than they did other times. Mary wondered why no parenting books suggested "communication through commuting." Car rides were a great time to talk.

But once she got to the class, it was different. To save time and gas and not spend the whole gymnastics class driving, Mary had to wait outside for her daughter. There was a little lobby, with doors to the changing area and a door to the gym, but it was truly little. There were three green chairs, a small table, and a few not-too-old magazines. Once in a while, some other mother was there, and they could chat. But mostly, the other mothers lived nearby. Their kids either came to gymnastics on their own, or the mothers dropped them off and went straight home. Sometimes, Mary went out to a Starbucks, but she was uncomfortable with sitting in a Starbucks for an hour at a time. Mostly, she brought her iPhone and a book, and waited.

Mary had plenty of time to think, waiting for her daughter outside the class. Not all of her thoughts were pleasant. The pain her daughter felt in the gymnastics class in their town—it was hard to think about it. And the town newspaper had a steady parade of letters about the dangers of the plant, notices about meetings to describe the dangers of the plant, and so forth. People didn't seem to write letters in favor of the plant.

Oh well. Who were "people," anyway? Those self-righteous little girls who had bullied her daughter? Her daughter was a "people." She was a "people," too. Maybe it was time to do something.

Mary began the letter on her iPhone, sending it to herself when she was done. When she went home, after dinner she would polish it and send it to the editor. She would ask her husband, of course, because he worked at the plant, and she didn't want to embarrass him in any way. She would have to check with him. But she was pretty sure it would be okay, and she was determined to do it. Send it in. Speak up for her daughter, and her husband, and herself.

Jennifer Barkley

THE LETTER BEGAN INAUSPICIOUSLY, looking like just another letter against nuclear energy.

"Fear of radiation from Fukushima . . ."

Yeah, yeah, Jennifer thought. Here we go again. Sometimes, she thought she would just have to retreat from the entire world. All of it. The woman in her yoga class. The newspaper that served her affluent town and the other towns near the river and the nuclear plant.

But she kept reading the letter, for some reason. The heading above it wasn't "Radiation from Fukushima," it was "Fear of Radiation from Fukushima." And the first paragraphs read:

"Fear of radiation from Fukushima has killed many Japanese, mostly elderly people. That's right: they were killed by fear and overreaction to the accident, not by radiation. Radiation hurt nobody outside the plant boundaries in the immediate aftermath. And looking at the future, international groups that have studied the incident say that excess cancers due to the radiation are extremely unlikely. But the Japanese held a panicky evacuation, in which elderly people were bundled into buses without their medicine and taken to holding centers where they had no access to warmth, water, or food for hours or days—this killed over 1,000 people. Panic killed people. Fear of radiation killed people.

"Unfortunately, some people in our town are showing the same sort of panic, teaching their children that our local plant is dangerous and only 'killers' would work there. Perhaps they should study the real lessons of Fukushima: panic and ignorance kill people."

Jennifer couldn't believe it. She read the letter twice. What a brave person had written that letter! She wondered . . . yes, the person lived in the town with the plant. Maybe the wife of someone who worked at the plant?

She read the letter again. It would be good to be friends with this person. Okay. What could she lose? "Mary Freeman." Her name and town were in the paper. Jennifer would give her a call, if she were in the phone book.

And Jennifer knew what was likely to happen. Within days, the people who thought that nuclear workers were "killers" would have their letters flooding in to the paper. She thought of her own husband: a proud Navy Nuke. People were teaching their children that people who worked at the plant were killers? Well, she believed they were teaching this, when she remembered the hatred in the eyes of that woman from yoga class.

"Killers?" It just wasn't right. People couldn't keep letting this kind of thing happen without even saying anything about it. Mary Freeman, whoever she was, had said something. She would give Mary a call.

Joseph Hayes

MARCH 11 WAS ALMOST upon them. The puppets would come, no doubt. Security was on top of it, including predicting a visit from the usual group of women who would chain themselves to the fence. Really, nothing had changed since last year.

But oddly, something had changed within Joseph himself. There had been letters, letters from women he didn't know, defending the plant and telling the truth about Fukushima: that nobody died, that panic had been more dangerous than radiation. One was from the wife of one of the operations guys, one of the men who was in training to be a licensed operator, as he recalled. Tim Freeman. But the other letter: who knew who it was from? Certainly not from anyone associated with the plant.

It was inspiring to see these letters. He thought about sending copies as internal email to the plant staff. Why not? Maybe some of them, and some of the spouses, would be inspired to write similar letters.

As a matter of fact, he was going to talk with the plant press liaison. There should be something better than usual they could say for their March 11 statement. Maybe he could make a stronger statement about the safety of the power plant and the integrity of the people who worked there. There must be some way to say it that had a better chance of being quoted, and not dismissed with "Plant spokesman denies."

The gifts of activism

THINGS DON'T HAPPEN IN QUITE so straightforward a fashion in the real world. And yet, in another way, they do. A few people taking a stand will inspire others to do the same. The positive feelings will grow, along with the feeling that you have friends and that your friends will support you. Rosa Parks refused to go to the back of the bus. "We must all hang together, or assuredly we shall all hang separately," Ben Franklin said before signing the Declaration of Independence.

Mary Freeman wrote a letter.

Being willing to speak out in public is key to being an activist. It's not easy to do. The first half of this book included many ways to speak out, to come out of the pro-nuclear closet and enter the world. The second half of the book is what you might call advanced activism. In most ways, in the second half, when you speak out in public, you will actually *be* in public, not just behind your computer.

I encourage you to read the second half of the book for plans and for inspiration. However, as I am trying to show with this Intermezzo, the relatively low-risk activities of the first part of the book can have profound effects.

Think of the second half of the book as a smorgasbord of choices. You can't do them all. What do *you* want to do?

Do what you are comfortable with. But do it.

WHITE PAPER 4

NUCLEAR ENERGY FOR EFFICIENT LAND USE

IF YOU'VE VISITED A nuclear power plant, you've probably noticed that the plant itself takes up relatively little space. When I think about land use for nuclear, I'm generally thinking about two main issues: the space required for renewables, and the daily mass-transport of fossil fuels.

Renewables

PER KWH PRODUCED, nuclear power uses far less land than renewables require. To analyze this, one can do various types of calculations.

Actually, before I did these types of calculations, back when I was in the renewables group at EPRI, it became painfully clear to me that renewables made very little power per unit. Well, back to the calculations . . .

Capacity factor refers to the ratio of a power plant's actual output over a period of time compared to its potential output if it operated at full capacity, continuously over the same period of time. If a plant runs most of the time, it might have a capacity factor of 90%. If it runs half the time, it has a capacity factor of 50%.

Wind turbines have a capacity factor of about 30%: they make power about 30% of the time. Nuclear plants have capacity factors of 90%. Therefore, to make the same number of kWh, it requires three times as many installed MW of wind turbines as installed MW of nuclear.

How much land would the wind turbines require?

Wind turbine spacing depends on many factors (whether they are on ridges or in flat farmland, for example). A 2009 report of the National Renewable Energy Laboratory summarizes the land use requirements as 34.5 plus or minus 22.4 hectares per MW installed.[69] (The figures are in table 1 of that report.) Let's use 34.5 hectares/MW, or 85 acres/MW.

Let's say we wanted to install enough wind turbines to make the same amount of energy as a small nuclear plant, such as Vermont Yankee (600 MW). We would need to install 1,800 MW of wind turbines. At 85 acres per MW, we would need 150,000 acres. In comparison, Green Mountain National Forest is about 400,000 acres.

This estimates assumes that wind turbines will be placed in the most compact groups possible. In Vermont, wind is higher and more useful on the ridges than in the valleys, and wind turbines are placed in lines and groups on the ridges. Therefore, a straight acreage calculation understates their impact on the land.

And of course, wind power isn't the same as nuclear power. Wind power wouldn't be as useful. The wind blows when it wants to blow, while power plants run when you need them to run.

I could go on with the acreage calculation, but it would be repetitive. I recommend the free book (if you download by pdf): *Sustainable Energy Without the Hot Air*, by Sir David MacKay.[70]

The MacKay book, often used as a text, calculates using renewables for energy in the United Kingdom. MacKay is very complete and very theoretical. For example, he imagines catching every drop of water that falls on the higher ground in Britain and having all this water run through hydro dams. In total, this would make 1.5 kWh per day, per person, in the United Kingdom.

For comparison, Britain uses 2,000 kWh per person per year, which is almost 7 kWh per day per person. Americans use about twice as much. Catching every drop of water for hydro isn't going to provide the British people with even minimum needs for electricity.[71]

I have done similar calculations. All these calculations show the same thing: we can't run a modern civilization on renewables alone. For example, I wrote "The 90% Solution" about Vermont's energy plan to get 90% of its energy from renewables.[72]

More about hydro

HYDRO POWER IS MUCH MORE useful than intermittent renewables like wind and solar. You can turn on hydro power when you need it (dispatch it). Hydro power is not at the whim of the wind blowing or the clouds scudding across the sky (and blocking the sun). There are many huge hydro projects in the US and elsewhere. You may have seen some of them.

However, seven out of ten of the biggest power plants in the United States are nuclear. Now, to get this result, we must judge the size of power plant by the *amount of power* it made each year. Seems sensible. If we judge the power plant by its "nameplate capacity," the maximum amount of power the plant can make, hydro plants are many of the biggest plants.

But they aren't the biggest—in terms of making power. Jim Conca at *Forbes* has an excellent post on this subject: "The Biggest Power Plants in America—Not What You Think."[73] Only one hydro plant, the Grand Coulee Dam, makes the list of ten plants that provide the most power.

This explained a phenomenon that puzzled me. We have only about 100 nuclear plants in the US, and they make about 20 percent of US electricity. They are so few and so small that you have to know where they are. If you don't know, you can drive all around the country and not see the nuclear plants.

On the other hand, US hydro projects make 7 percent of our electricity, and they are all over the place. The Columbia, the Colorado, the Tennessee Valley Authority, the poor old Connecticut River outside my window (I can see the 43 MW Wilder Dam). And all that very visible hydro adds up to 7 percent of our electricity.

As I noted in a blog post, our little Vermont Yankee plant, now closed down, whose output the opponents loved to denigrate as not important to the grid—Vermont Yankee made more kWh per year when it was operating then the Hoover Dam made per year. This is despite the fact that the Hoover Dam is huge, and it is backed up by the largest reservoir in the US: Lake Mead.

Yes, Vermont Yankee made more power per year than the Hoover Dam.[74]

Fossil

MACKAY HAS LED THE WAY on land-use measurements for renewables. I do not know of a similar source for fossil. But let's face it: uranium has thousands of times the energy content per kilogram than coal has. We don't have huge uranium strip mines, mountaintop removal uranium mining, "unit trains" of uranium cars heading east from Wyoming. That's what coal needs, not nuclear.

I can't tell how much land is used for oil and gas drilling, pipelines, and how much rail transport of oil takes place. I just remember the tens of coal cars per day going to our local coal plant, compared to the three semi-trucks arriving at our local nuclear plant every eighteen months.

Size matters. Nuclear has the lightest effect on the land.

CHAPTER NINETEEN

THE PHILOSOPHY OF SPEAKING IN PUBLIC

THESE NEXT CHAPTERS are about activism in public—right out there with people. The previous chapters were about activism from behind your computer.

There are advantages to staying right behind your computer. There are also profound advantages to stepping out in public, because you will meet like-minded people. As you move from occasionally having a letter in the paper to attending pro-nuclear events, you will find yourself with more opportunities to speak in public.

Remember, nuclear advocacy is not a linear path anyway. Advocacy is a bazaar, a department store, a grocery store, or a smorgasbord—whatever you want to call it. In other words, you pick and choose what *you* want to do. If you are becoming more visible in the community, opportunities to speak will begin to appear.

So, now a look at your options when you step out of the closet and onto the bigger stage of the world. Or perhaps, your options when you step onto a real stage—or at least, somewhere with a microphone.

The philosophy of speaking in public

THE PHILOSOPHY is quite simple, and we have seen it before. Here it is:

Your ability to speak in public is valuable.

This chapter is about why it is valuable for ordinary people to speak up for the nuclear industry. This is because, in many cases, the nuclear industry cannot speak for itself.

I give an example from my own history.

My first debate

WHEN I BEGAN SPEAKING in public, I was sort of thrown into deep water pretty fast. I am not exactly sure how it happened, but the first real speaking engagement I remember was a debate.

A League of Women Voters group in New Hampshire was going to have a debate about Vermont Yankee and nuclear power in general. They had a man from an opponent organization lined up, and another man who was retired from a utility commission in New Hampshire. The opponent was taking the "shut them all down" side, as his organization usually does. The retired commissioner was supposed to be the voice of dispassionate decision making. They needed someone in favor of nuclear power.

They asked the local power plants (Seabrook, Vermont Yankee), and both said they were not sending anyone. This is pretty standard. A debate situation is somewhat uncontrolled, and most corporations prefer to issue press releases or hold a press conference, where a carefully coached executive can answer questions. A debate in a library can lead to a utility representative saying something that is a little off but highly quotable. This can lead to no end of trouble. No utility or big business is likely to send their people out to debate a "shut them down" representative.

Oddly, the moderator was not aware of the fact that businesses don't debate. He was upset that the power plants were dissing him (as he thought). Meanwhile, he had a more pressing problem: people were going to show up, and who was going to represent the pro-nuclear point of view?

One of the moderator's friends was also a friend of mine, and this man suggested me to the moderator. I could be the pro-nuclear person. I was not all that well known, but I was thinking about starting a blog, and I had written some letters to the editor.

In desperation, the moderator called me, and I said yes. Well, that ended the moderator's desperation, and transferred the desperation to me!

Okay, I'll do it

I WASN'T SURE HOW IT WOULD GO, but I looked up some of the images that I was sure the opponents would use (for example, the collapsed cooling tower at Vermont Yankee). I used those images myself and explained them. This worked very well. It disconcerted the opponent and took away a lot of his thunder when he used the same image. (As it happened, I spoke first, usually the weaker position. I was worried about that, because it meant I wouldn't be in a position to rebut. So I started with a rebuttal.)

However, overall, the debate was a difficult experience, because I had never done it before, and people were watching. But I held my own, because I had facts on my side.

There's only one thing good about being thrown into deep water as your first experience. After that, everything else looks easy. Afterwards, I had the feeling that if I could do that debate, I could do anything. If you find yourself in deep water right off the bat, you will do fine. But I hope that is not your first experience.

Another take-away from this story, however, is that the nuclear industry needs advocates out there to speak up. There are many situations in which the plant itself is constrained from speaking. But you can speak. They can call the guy from the anti-nuclear organization, and they can call you.

ACTION ITEM:

Imagine an official and an unofficial response. Think about an anti-nuclear statement. Think of how a big business (power plant) will have to respond to it. Think about how you can respond. Realize your value as an unofficial supporter.

CHAPTER TWENTY

BEING IN THE AUDIENCE

You don't have to speak

If you don't want to speak, that is fine. Be there anyway. Sit next to your team and be a clear supporter. You are doing a lot because you are making sure that there are some friendly faces for the pro-nuclear people to see, when they look at the crowd.

Sit with friends

Try to make early arrangements with friends, to come there, to meet there, to sit together. I hate to be so blunt, but there is both psychological and physical safety in numbers. You want to be with your friends. Sometimes the opponents come close to (or cross the line of) assault: not fierce punches, but slaps or throwing manure. You are less likely to be one of the targets if you are sitting in a group.

(If a nuclear opponent reads this, he or she will probably say this only happens because they are so frustrated at not being heard. Okay. Actually, opponents are HEARD all the time. Some of them get very frustrated at not being OBEYED. At any rate, frustrated people sometimes get physical. At that point, hopefully, some other people restrain them, maybe the police. And perhaps the opponents can be sent to anger management classes. End of rant. But I have heard that excuse so often.)

Sit together, the more the merrier.

The many virtues of t-shirts

THE T-SHIRT EXPERIENCE. Something else that is useful: you will not know all the nuclear advocates who will attend these meetings. I am always surprised. Quietly, without much fuss, people who are in favor of nuclear energy show up. But how will they know you are in favor of nuclear energy, also?

TV cameras may be scanning the room: how will they know you are there?

A TV or radio reporter may be looking out for a pro-nuclear person to interview. How will she know you are there?

The answer is often t-shirts. Make some t-shirts up in advance. Some examples are "Californians for Green Nuclear Power,"[75] which made green t-shirts with the outlines of Diablo Canyon. For my group, I made white t-shirts that said, "Safe Reliable Economical" and had the "Nuclear Power Yes Please" logo. For a hearing, a college group from ANS made royal blue t-shirts saying, "American Nuclear Society."[76]

Don't forget vests and hats. For example, anti-wind protestors supported a ban-the-turbines bill at a press conference in the State House in Vermont. The protestors wore green vests. Vests can be a great idea, because you can put them on *over* business clothes. Not everyone wants to wear a t-shirt. At a meeting where union workers supported a new build for Calvert Cliffs, they wore light-green vests and dark-green baseball caps.[77]

When the reporters scan the room, or when the pro-nuclear person wanders in and hopes she is not alone . . . be visible.

I prefer white or light-colored t-shirts, or strong colors like blue, green, or yellow. The nuclear opponents are very fond of vigils and sorrow. They often appear in all black, or even all-black with masks or skeletons. Their choice. Make sure nobody can confuse you with them. You are on the side of light and life! Look like it.

Beyond t-shirts

BIG BUTTONS ARE HELPFUL: I have a bunch of buttons that say VY4VT. The power plant made those. An individual woman made some other great buttons: her buttons said "Yes Vermont Yankee." (No, it wasn't me making those buttons. It is the name of my blog, but I was surprised at the buttons.)

With buttons, it is important that they be big and bright enough to see. For example, they should be visible from the front of the room or by a reporter. Sometimes buttons are better than t-shirts. Buttons are "a random group of people," while in some cases, t-shirts can look like "the planned group of supporters, not ordinary people at all." Use your own judgment on this.

What about signs? In most hearing rooms, people are forbidden to take large objects (such as signs) into the room. Big signs can be used as weapons, so they are banned. (We will talk a little more about signs when we discuss rallies.) Something you can do (it's cheating a bit, but I have seen the opponents do it) is carry a small cardboard sign, no bigger than a piece of paper, in your briefcase. Your friends can carry them also. You can pull them out to support your speaker. (The opponents pull their signs out to harass pro-nuclear speakers.) The security people will not take them away, because they are clearly harmless. Nobody is fearful of small pieces of cardboard being used as assault weapons.

If you can have a table outside the room, with cookies and flyers and information, this can be great. For example, Suzy Hobbs Baker arranged ahead of time to have a table at a public meeting about the Lee nuclear station. She had some of her pro-nuclear artwork on the table, along with cookies to entice people. She is an artist and was wearing one of her pro-nuclear t-shirts. Art and signs can be present, but often outside the meeting room.[78]

Why you are doing this

WHY ARE YOU AT THE MEETING when you won't speak? You are there because people don't want to be alone. People who are speaking pro-nuclear (and hopefully, you will choose to be one of them, at some time) don't want to look out over a room full of unfriendly faces. By showing up and being very visible, you will offer tremendous support to those who are speaking. You will show the reporters that there are two sides to the story and two sets of people who are passionate about it.

This is part of the smorgasbord of opportunities you will have, and frankly, it is a fun one. Next, we will talk about the next possibility at the smorgasbord. If you decide to speak.

ACTION ITEM:

Accessorize. Do you have some kind of pro-nuclear pin available? Can you get one from your local nuclear facility?

CHAPTER TWENTY-ONE

HOW TO SPEAK IN PUBLIC, AN OVERVIEW

SPEAKING IN PUBLIC IS A learning-by-doing experience. It's also pretty frightening to start a chapter titled "How to Speak in Public." What if I say the wrong things?

My fear about starting this chapter is a lot like fear of speaking in public.

Two parts to the fear

YOU CAN DIVIDE THE FEAR of speaking in public into two parts. The first part is the fear of saying something wrong, of making a fool of oneself. The second part is the fear that people won't like what you are saying and, in consequence, won't like you.

Although the blood pounding in the ears, shortness of breath, high heart rate, and nausea that these fears can bring is out of proportion with the actual threat level of speaking in a public place, both fears have some basis in fact. Yes, you may make a mistake. It happens. Yes, some people opposed to nuclear energy won't like what you have to say, and maybe they won't like you.

Luckily for your speaking career, the things that you do to overcome the first fear will also make you a better speaker.

Also, before we start any chapter, I want to emphasize that these chapters are meant to be helpful, not prescriptive. Nuclear advocacy is a smorgasbord of activities, and you get to choose which ones you participate in. Participating in *any* activity is worthwhile.

And so, with that note, off we go to Speaking in Public.

Overcoming the fear of making a mistake

FIRST OFF, YOU WILL NEVER totally overcome this fear. Part of this fear is stage fright, which has very little to do with what you plan to say on the stage. I took aikido from a sensei who said, "If you have butterflies in your stomach, make them fly in formation."

Another way to look at it is that pretty much every person who goes on the stage or performs in a concert has stage fright. Eventually, for most people, it moves down to the level of "pre-concert jitters" and does not prevent getting out there and performing. The problem is that people who never perform on stage don't get to witness the rituals and amulets of the people who do perform, just before they step in front of an audience. From the audience, it looks easy.

But, as long as you don't set the bar too high ("I will be cool as a cucumber" is too high), you can indeed overcome much of your stage fright and your fear of making a mistake.

And now for the unexpected words of wisdom on how to do this:

- Prepare
- Practice

What? You knew that was coming? Well, then, you already knew how to overcome stage fright.

First: Prepare

DECIDE WHAT YOU ARE going to say. For the moment, I am assuming you will make a statement at some sort of meeting. Usually, there is a limit of perhaps three minutes for that statement. You don't have a lot of time. You can basically make only one point. For some excellent examples (if I do say so myself), see the statements that many people made in favor of Vermont Yankee at a Public Service Board hearing. My husband and I collected these statements in a book, *Voices for Vermont Yankee*.[79]

Some of the people who spoke at that hearing had a highly technical background. Most of them did not. However, they all had their own reasons, and their own stories, about why they supported Vermont Yankee. You also have your own story. Speak from your experience, and your history, and your story. When you speak in these terms, your words will be powerful and credible.

Once you have decided on the point you are making, write down the important subtopics about that point (see Point of View Plus Two in the next chapter). You might have lots of facts to present (this facility will prevent this many tons of CO_2 from entering the atmosphere), or you might stress feelings more than verifiable facts (our local plant gives us a solid economic base for the vibrant music scene in our town). Whether facts or feelings are at the center, write down whatever facts you need. Make certain of them. Knowing exactly what you are talking about improves both your talk and your self-confidence.

Now, at this stage, you have to choose how to prepare your actual words. The calmest and safest way is to write down your statement, carry it into the meeting, and read it out loud. (Another advantage of written remarks is that you can hand the written statement to the recorder at the meeting.) Any stiffness that reading aloud brings will be more than balanced by your internal confidence that you are saying what you want to say. Umm . . . not trying to scare you, but the opponents may boo or shout while you are speaking. Sticking to the script can be a blessing.

Now that I have said that, I always use a list of facts or talking points, merely a few words or facts scribbled on a piece of paper. I feel more at ease this way, for some reason. I want to be clear, but not appear too distant, reading from a page of paper. On the other hand, with this technique, heckling sometimes makes me unable to finish what I was saying.

This business of speaking in public is not always easy.

Speak Simply

WHEN YOU SPEAK, speak simply.

- Make one point.
- Try to make that point with analogies to something people know about.
- Tell a story, if you can.
- Don't use jargon.

Richard Trudell speaks at Vermont Public Service Board hearing, Vernon VT, November 7, 2012

Analogies can be very effective. Here's an analogy using baseball players. When Richard Trudell, an engineer in Vermont, made a statement for Vermont Yankee, he said that Yankee has a great hitting record (it is online reliably), while the new recruits (renewables) have a poor batting average, and won't even suit up without a subsidy.[80]

There is always some tension between presenting technical information and telling memorable anecdotes. There is no "best" answer here. I think it is a matter of personal style. If you share technical information, don't make it too full of jargon. Anecdotes have to be short and relevant. Whatever works for you will be best for your communication, because it is what *you* are most comfortable with. Analogies can sometimes bridge this gap.

Another useful method for organizing your thoughts is to use "benefits statements."

Think benefits statement

AN EASY WAY TO PREPARE short remarks is to plan your remarks as a "benefits statement." An old advertising saying describes this: "Don't list the features, describe the benefits."

Advertisers don't write, "There are two types of abrasives and two types of bleaching agents in this toothpaste." These statements are about features. They are descriptions of the product. People basically don't care about features. (And those abrasives sound scary.)

Instead, advertisers write about the benefits: "For a gleaming bright smile, use this toothpaste!"

The "gleaming bright smile" is the benefit. The advertisement may back up the benefits statement with more facts such as "specially formulated to be whiten even badly stained teeth." But even the facts will refer back to the benefits statement.

Yes, of course. I know. You are not writing an ad for toothpaste. You are planning to make a pro-nuclear statement. In general, however, the same idea basically works.

For example, here's a feature statement about nuclear power: "Nuclear has the greatest capacity factor of any type of power plant. You can count on nuclear plants for reliable baseload power."

Just as in the toothpaste case, this nuclear *feature* statement has jargon ("capacity factor, baseload") that is off-putting (like "two types of abrasives").

It's easy to reframe this statement into a benefits statement. The benefits statement is more personal and less technical but says basically the same thing.

Here's a benefits statement on the same subject: nuclear reliability. "Nuclear plants help me feel more secure in the winter, because even in the coldest weather, nuclear power plants run steadily. During the polar vortex, the nuclear plants provided reliable electricity while other types of plants struggled with fuel deliveries."

Reframing into "benefits statements" can be fun: at least, I enjoy it. Almost anything I want to say about nuclear power can be restated as a benefits statement if I choose to do so.

I don't always make a benefits statement, but I find the exercise is helpful even when I end up with a feature statement. I usually start by thinking of the feature I want to discuss. Next, I try to think about how this feature helps people (how it *benefits* people). This exercise helps me express myself more clearly, with less jargon. Whether I make a benefits statement or a factual statement, thinking about the benefits helps me express myself more clearly.

So now you are prepared. You know what you want to say. It isn't too long. You know how to express it in simple terms.

And now it is time to . . .

Practice

PRACTICE IN FRONT OF THE MIRROR. Or don't. Practice without the mirror. Ask your spouse to listen to you. Practice with friends.

Or don't practice. Some people don't need to and, indeed, feel their talk loses all its freshness if they practice.

Whether you practice or not, emphasize the following when you get up to speak:

- Be honest.
- Stay calm.

If you are in a position where you may be asked questions, just say what you know and do not speculate or get pulled into talking about hypothetical situations.

Speak and then shut up

WHEN ANSWERING QUESTIONS:

Don't speculate.

For example, one of the first times I was interviewed about Vermont Yankee, I was asked to speculate, and I foolishly did. The interviewer asked me what would happen if used fuel bundles fell in the Connecticut River. I was taken aback, because the used fuel bundles are stored a long way from the river, above the 200-year flood zone and so forth. There's no credible way for them to get in the river.

I gave a fairly reasonable answer. ("I guess you would just fish them out again. The fuel is ceramic that has already been immersed in water for at least ten years: it isn't going to dissolve or anything.") I got away fairly well on that one, but it could have been worse. People will come up with all sorts of unrealistic scenarios. You don't have to follow them and try to refute them. Stick to what you know. "The fuel is stored safely. It's not about to fall in the river."

My friend Fritz Schneider is an award-winning media specialist with Clark Communications in Maryland. If he had been with me that day, he would have told me to state my point and then STOP! Reporters are trained to stare at you after you made your point, hoping you will continue to talk. Schneider says that many of the "I was misquoted" problems come from elaborations you might make while the reporter remains surprisingly silent. State your point, and then . . . stop.

Your story, and your honesty, are your credibility.

ACTION ITEM:

Find your story. Write three things you would like people to know about nuclear energy. Write down how you yourself learned these things (your story).

CHAPTER TWENTY-TWO

QUICK AND SIMPLE SPEAKING TOOLS

MANY PEOPLE WHO HAVE TO speak in public do more than practice—they also get formal speaker training, usually from their employer. This chapter is a quick and simple version of some of that training, and you can use these tools when talking to reporters, debating, or talking to groups.

In preparing for public speaking, the good news is that some of the most important speeches are also the shortest ones. If you get in front of a cameraman at a rally or other event, you won't get much time to talk, and if you do talk in a lengthy fashion, you won't know what part of your words will make it into the film clip. In short, it is time for your elevator speech.

The elevator speech

CONSIDER THIS: YOU DISTRIBUTED a fantastic press release announcing your St. Patrick's Day rally, and a local TV camera crew has arrived at the rally to interview you. Their first question will likely be something like, "Jane, you're hosting a rally in support of this nuclear plant. Tell us why you're here today." You can't very well say, "Read this press release." You also won't have time to read the press release to the TV reporter.

Tamar Cerafici, a lawyer with extensive utility and nuclear experience, points out that preparing a speech for a rally is just as important as preparing one for a public hearing or meeting. When activists connect with reporters, it's very important to have an elevator speech prepared in advance.

The elevator speech is a clear, brief message or "commercial" about your organization or the issue you're supporting. It is typically about thirty seconds. The name comes from the amusing idea that it's the same short speech you'd give someone if you only had a thirty-second elevator ride.

Here's a possible elevator speech for this particular occasion:

"My name is Jane Doe, president of Granite Staters for Clean Air. We're here because we support the continued operation of (PLANT). (PLANT) powers more than one million homes, without any air pollution or greenhouse gases. This plant is a real asset to our clean air and the high quality of life we enjoy here in the Granite State."

In Jane's elevator speech she did three things: she established her credibility as a member of Granite Staters for Clean Air, provided simple facts supported by industry data, and finished by tying clean air to quality of life in New Hampshire.

Short and succinct. Credibility and one main idea. An elevator speech.

Okay. I admit it. The first time I heard about "an elevator speech," the idea scared me. How could I be that quick and precise? But I now realize that we use elevator speeches all the time—when we're at a job interview, when we meet someone new, when we're on the phone with Comcast. We state who we are, what we're about, or what we want. We have all had a lot of practice making "elevator speeches." When you remember this about yourself, preparing a speech about the plant will be much easier.

What if you need to speak a bit longer? For example, at a Rotary Club or on some kind of panel about energy?

The next step after an elevator speech is Point of View Plus Two (POV+2, for short): an excellent way to organize short remarks. (Or long remarks, if that is necessary.)

Point of View Plus Two

THIS IS A POWERFUL speaking approach. Edward Kee shared this insight with me. Kee owns Nuclear Economics Consulting Group, and he has extensive experience in addressing meetings and answering questions. Using POV+2, you make a short, simple declarative statement or assertion that is followed immediately with two (maybe three) supporting facts. Here are some examples:

Vermont Yankee does not face Fukushima issues.
- It is far from any body of water that could have a tsunami.
- There are multiple independent sources of AC power for cooling.
- The operator has on-site portable generators and pumps.

Did you personally verify the data in these analyses are correct?

- No. I delegated the data review to others.
- Two separate teams each did an independent verification.
- Both teams found that the data was correct.

Point of View Plus Two can be used very effectively in public meetings and even in expert testimony—it is also a way to answer a question directly, plus make a couple of additional points. POV+2 is often used in training courses for consultants at the largest firms.

With discipline, POV+2 is a powerful rhetorical technique. However, most of us find it difficult to limit our remarks to short and sharp points. It also may be hard to come up with short points in real time. In other words, POV+2 will require some practice and preparation.

How do you get to Carnegie Hall? Practice, man, practice.

Loaded questions

WELL, NOW THAT WE HAVE, ever so gingerly, edged into the question of answering questions, we need to address the issues of questions that imply something bad about the plant. In other words, how do we deal with the loaded question? Some reporters, many anti-nuclear activists, and even some ordinary people will ask you questions like this. The classic loaded-question example is when the prosecutor asks, "Have you stopped beating your wife?" If the accused answers, "yes," that implies his guilt—but so does "no." Alas, this type of question is a standard rhetorical technique of some anti-nuclear interviewers.

But there is a simple technique to block these questions and get yourself back to communicating solid information. The technique is called "blocking and bridging."

Block and bridge

AS YOU CONTINUE TO SUPPORT your local facility, your information base will grow. But, especially in the beginning, it is important to use your knowledge to the fullest by blocking and bridging. You *block* what they want to talk about and *bridge* back to what you want to talk about. There will be more about this in the sections on how to be effective in public, but for now, realize that if you have even a short but solid list of your own points, you are golden.

An example:

You don't know everything about Price-Anderson. You get asked about Price-Anderson, which is a government-mandated requirement that nuclear plants must buy extensive liability insurance. You get asked about it in an aggressive fashion. Block that line of inquiry and get back to what you *do* know about: the safety of nuclear plants.[81]

"Thank you for asking about Price-Anderson. In over forty years, that act has not cost the taxpayers a penny for claims against commercial nuclear reactors, so it is always a rather theoretical discussion (block). However, questions about that policy are actually, at their heart, questions about nuclear safety (bridge). Statistics show that nuclear plants are the safest . . ."

I have assumed that safety is one of your talking points and you have those statistics. You are now talking about what *you* want to talk about. You have bridged to it.

A couple of things about blocking and bridging. You are not dodging the question; you are merely moving on. You don't ignore the question, you answer it briefly and don't spend much time on it before going to your own talking point.

But what if you don't know much about the original question? If you don't know anything about the topic, say so. Then go on to bridging to what you know about. "Others in my group are experts on Price-Anderson, and I am not. But I have noticed that questions about Price-Anderson are actually, at their heart, questions about nuclear safety . . ."

I had this technique used and overused on me in a debate, and I can say it was effective. My opponent used it far more aggressively than I would be comfortable with doing. His "blocking and bridging" was more like "dodging and changing the subject." At any rate, it was effective. The example of how it was used was instructive.

Vermont Yankee had a forty-year license, which was extended by the NRC. However, while the extension was still pending, one man I debated kept coming back to his mantra of "a deal is a deal, and forty years was the deal." No matter what I said about anything, he always returned to "a deal is a deal."

Pro-nuclear people can use this same technique, but more gently. We don't dodge a question, but we don't have to talk endlessly in response to "Have you stopped beating your wife?"-type questions. We can answer these questions briefly and then move on to the subjects we know and care about.

We will talk more about debating techniques later, but for now, let's just note that you have to have *good* talking points, but you don't have to have an infinite number of them. When asked a loaded question, you can bridge back to the points you are planning to make.

ACTION ITEM:

Practice your skills. Prepare an elevator speech as if you had sent a press release about a St. Patrick's Day rally in support of the plant.

Imagine someone asks you the plant-equivalent of "Have you stopped beating your wife?" and block and bridge to the plant's safety record.

CHAPTER TWENTY-THREE

SPEAKING AT A HEARING

EARLIER CHAPTERS ON speaking in public covered many aspects of speaking at a hearing. For example:

- Preparing short remarks
- Taking the remarks with you, in some form
- Going with friends
- Sitting together
- Being visible with insignia or t-shirts
- Clearly being a team

This chapter will cover some more on "being a team" but will also consider more issues about your own feelings and emotional state at the hearing. To communicate effectively, you need to start by acknowledging and managing your own emotions.

Do you have to speak?

LET ME FIRST NOTE THAT MANY hearings have two ways to contribute: go to the hearing or send in a comment on the docket. In the chapter on blogging, I have a section on "calls to action." One call to action is to ask followers to send comments into a docket. Many organizations have open comment periods for dockets, proposed rulings, or proposed rules. You can ask people to comment via Facebook, and you can show people example comments on your blog. This is an excellent way to be an activist from behind your computer. Do it! You can probably encourage a dozen people to comment on a docket for every person you can expect to show up, in person, at a hearing.

But there's nothing like "being there." Also, the hearing will probably be covered in the press, and so your comment and your presence will get a wider audience. The rest of this section assumes you have stepped away from your computer, and you are there, right there, in person, at the hearing. But before we start, I did want to point out that there are other ways to comment. Activism is a smorgasbord, for sure.

Being a team

IN PREPARATION FOR A HEARING, it is good, but not essential, that team members communicate about what you are planning to say. If eight pro-nuclear people decide to talk about how nuclear prevents carbon dioxide from entering the atmosphere, but nobody talks about how it prevents acid gases (NOx and SOx) from entering the atmosphere, and nobody talks about the jobs it provides to its local community—that is not the best way to present at a hearing. You want to provide a range of powerful comments in favor of nuclear energy, not just the same comment over and over. I recommend looking at the book *Voices for Vermont Yankee* for an example of the range of possible comments.[82]

After you have your talking points together, have a call or a meeting or an email exchange where people exchange sentences that describe what they plan to say at the hearing. This will give a better view of what is going to happen at the meeting. Plus, communicating with each other before the hearing will help each person in the team gain confidence in their message and in the team message. Also, if nobody is covering a main point (hopefully, you all have talking points available), someone can step up to cover it.

On the other hand, if you decided to just show up at the meeting, everyone with her own notes, that is good also. My experience is that pro-nuclear people have very careful and very individual reasons for supporting nuclear energy, and any group of people will say different things, useful things, not echoing each other.

I do my best to be respectful of what anti-nuclear people say at these hearings, but after a while, it gets a little boring for me. Almost all anti-nuclear testimony can be restated as "Radiation is very dangerous and I am very afraid."

For example, I admit that I had a hard time not chuckling at one woman. This was at one of the first hearings I ever attended. This woman said she had moved near Vermont Yankee thirty years before, along with many of her friends. (Maybe a commune? I don't know.) And back then, when they moved, she and all of her friends were very healthy. And now, many of them were sick! This was due to the presence of Vermont Yankee, in her opinion. She left out the major variable: everybody is now thirty years older than when they moved to Vermont! Most people are shocked if a 25-year-old gets cancer or heart disease (she lumped all illnesses together), but most of us are not as surprised if a 55-year-old develops these conditions. If you take a quiz on health at a doctor's office, it will almost certainly ask if you consider yourself in good health "for your age."

This woman left thirty years out of the equation.

Your group's statements will be better than hers. As I said earlier, whatever your pro-nuclear group says, whether they talk about the statements ahead of time or not, your statements will be miles ahead of the opposing testimony. So just do it.

Another thing a team can do is watch your back. For example, you are speaking and someone begins loud booing, drowning you out. If you have a good moderator in the meeting, the moderator will take care of it. In some meetings, you will be on your own. In that case, the people on your team are the ones who can help you. You may not want to turn around and say, "Be quiet," but someone on your team can shout, "Let him speak!" or something like that.

To some extent, a team is a mini-army. You support and protect each other. I consider some meetings to be "bring your own army" meetings. I remember one meeting where, in order to protect NRC staff members, the local police stood between the NRC people and the crowd. Still in this protective configuration, the police escorted the NRC staff out of the room. Nuclear opponents had moved to the front of the room and surrounded the staff members. The leader

Police lead NRC people from meeting room, for their protection. (NRC people at right of picture.) Anti-nuclear activists surround microphones at front of room. NRC meeting, May 23, 2012, Brattleboro, Vermont

of the opponents was interviewed later. Some reports had said that the meeting had "gotten out of hand." However, when interviewed, the opponent leader said she had planned to disrupt the meeting.[83]

In some meetings, anti-nuclear people shout, throw manure, or run at people in an intimidating way, as if they are just about to attack someone. In some meetings, the moderators let them get away with this. So, sit with your friends. Cover each other's backs. If you are in such a meeting, you might choose to leave. Or you might be able to handle it, if you "bring your own army."

Another hint: Speak early

USUALLY, THE ORDER IN WHICH people speak will be determined by a sign-up sheet. Get to the meeting early, if you can, and sign up to be one of the earliest speakers.

Supporters and opponents lining up for sign-up sheet at Vermont Public Service Board hearing, Vernon, VT, November 7, 2012

There are several reasons to speak near the beginning of the meeting, including having the simple joy of "getting it over with." Mimi Holland Limbach of Potomac Communications Group describes a very important reason to speak early: reporters rarely stay to the end of a multi-hour meeting. From the reporters' point of view, the speakers in the first hour are often—the story of the meeting.

If nuclear opponents have taken all the early speaking slots, the media will likely report that the meeting was filled with angry citizens who criticized the plant. If supporters fill at least some of the early slots, the reporting is likely to be more balanced. What happens in the third hour of the meeting is far less likely to be reported in the press.

So get to the meeting early, and sign up for an early speaking slot. You will be less anxious (less waiting), and your words will be more likely to influence the media story of the meeting.

Keep calm and carry on

YOU ARE THERE TO SPEAK your truth. It isn't necessarily going to be an easy task. If you have high blood pressure to start with, attending hearings may be one part of the activism smorgasbord where you might choose to walk away from the table.

Still, most people can attend these hearings. You need to sit with friends: a sure way to reduce anxiety. You need to remember to breathe: it is surprisingly easy to find yourself holding your breath during some outrageous set of statements, but that never helps. You are prepared, so you can speak.

You are there so the people holding the hearing, and the people who are reporting on the hearing, and the people who may be watching it on community television, will realize that many people in the room are in favor of nuclear energy. Nuclear opponents like to divide the world into "good people who oppose nuclear" and "people who work for nuclear and are desperate to keep their jobs." The purpose of your group, among other things, is to show that the world is not so easily divided.

Keep calm and be respectful

BASICALLY, TO INFLUENCE PEOPLE, you should
- Keep calm yourself

- Respect the other person

Most successful politicians know this. They don't get upset, and they respect the other person enough to not offend them. That way, when another vote comes up where the two "enemies" can agree with each other . . . they can agree with each other. And both politicians become more effective.

Being respectful doesn't mean being a doormat. People who are very skilled at getting *their* point across will oppose you. You have the right to ask them, in front of the crowd, to "Please stop interrupting me." At one point, in one meeting, things were getting unruly and very noisy. At that point someone shouted, "This is what democracy looks like!" I went to an empty microphone and spoke into it, quite out of turn. I said that democracy actually means that various voices are heard, not just one side.[84]

These are all respectful things to do. What is not respectful is booing during someone else's speech (no matter if you disagree) or ad hominem attacks. I am sometimes opposed by a man whose technical background is being a high school art teacher. That is . . . he hasn't got a technical background. I never mention this when we are both talking at the same meeting. "I am a scientist and you aren't" never won anyone to your side. Also, the statement would be disrespectful of his self-education on nuclear issues.

I address what he said, not the fact that this man said it. Many scientists don't do this, and then they are surprised when other citizens consider scientists to be elitist. All our votes are worth the same, when you get right down to it.

True confession: I am not perfect at this.

Emotional motivations

ALSO, MANY OF THE PEOPLE you are facing have very personal reasons for the positions they take. The reason that they make all these emotional and basically unsupportable arguments is that they have strong feelings. They believe that nuclear energy has caused and will cause untold harm to people they care about, including themselves.

Let me give you an example. One man is an anti-nuclear commentator on many blogs. He is absolutely relentlessly anti-nuclear, and he keeps coming back. Once he has started commenting on a blog post, he tends to keep coming back to comment until he has the last word.

From email conversations with him, I have learned that his daughter died of cancer. I am pretty sure he believes this is due to Chernobyl. There is (in my opinion) no reason to believe that anyone in Europe died of cancer due to Chernobyl. I also suspect this man was seriously anti-nuclear before his daughter became ill. Still, I see his behavior as his tribute to his daughter. This makes it easier to be polite to him.

Another anti-nuclear person, this time in America, often says that with nuclear plants around, we pay our utility bills at the hospital. Her husband also died of cancer.

Please understand that I am not saying that you have to let a troll take over your blog comments, or let people interrupt you when you are speaking, or let people claim that nuclear plants are causing huge outbreaks of cancer, widespread death of sea creatures in the Pacific, or other false statements. I am merely saying that it is best to refute the words, while behaving respectfully to the people. They often have deep emotional reasons for what they do. If they behave disrespectfully to you, point it out in a way that other people will notice. "Please stop interrupting."

As emotions run high, and you begin to feel under attack, this is pretty hard to do. You will not do it perfectly. But if you manage, even imperfectly, to keep your cool, that is a victory.

Stick up for yourself and your position, and don't go on the attack. People are watching. Some people are rooting for the person who is interrupting you, but most people will be impressed with your relatively calm response.

Books about communication

THERE ARE MANY BOOKS about speaking in public, and about speaking to people who disagree with you. An old one, but still extremely well written and valid, is Dale Carnegie's *How to Win Friends and Influence People*.[85] A newer book, which includes animations on the web to illustrate its points, is *Crucial Conversations, Tools for Talking When the Stakes Are High*.[86] I am not going to try to make this short section the equivalent of these excellent books.

David Ropeik is an expert on risk communication. He has several books available, and looks at risk communication as part of Relationship Management. Ropeik is clear that "over-reassuring" is a bad strategy. "There will be no more Zika cases!" That doesn't work. Putting the situation in context works; over-reassuring does not work.[87]

Again, whether you read these books or not, in order to influence people:

- Keep calm yourself
- Respect the other person

That is the ultimate secret.

Some people do change

ANOTHER REASON TO BEHAVE respectfully: you never know who might change his or her mind. Gwyneth Cravens is the author of *Power to Save the World*, which is, in my opinion, the *best* pro-nuclear book.[88]

It describes her journey from anti-nuclear activist to supporter of nuclear energy. Cravens' first experience with this relatively new source of electricity was simple: she was terrified by the accident at the Three Mile Island plant and later joined protests against opening the Shoreham nuclear plant. But when she learned more about the science of nuclear power, she changed her views. She learned the facts, mainly because one knowledgeable pro-nuclear scientist gently and respectfully explained to her the environmental and other benefits of nuclear power.

You never know who may change their mind. You can't read anyone else's thoughts. Don't let anyone walk on you, but don't insult them, either. What goes around, comes around.

ACTION ITEM:

Communication. Read a book or web post about communication. Make a note of what struck you about what the author said.

CHAPTER TWENTY-FOUR

WRITING A PRESS RELEASE

IN THE INTERMEZZO, Plant Manager Joseph Hayes begins thinking about how he can improve a normally drab press release into a memorable one. He wants to take a stronger stance on the lessons learned from Fukushima and the improvements made across the industry, and at his nuclear plant.

He's on the right track to earning more balanced media coverage by sharing a proactive, positive story about his plant. Instead of hiding under his desk waiting for another "plant spokespersons deny" statement, he is taking charge and sharing real information, upbeat information about his plant.

Writing a press release can seem a bit intimidating, but it's not much different than a letter to the editor. Here are some steps to sending a press release.

Decide on the topic

A PRESS RELEASE IS AN opportunity to have the voice of your organization heard in the media. There are many occasions when your group might distribute a press release. For example:

- In recognition of a positive historical event or anniversary. This can be the plant's anniversary of going online or some other milestone, such as a breaker-to-breaker run. Or the first day the first commercial reactor went online in the United States. In this case, you can describe the benefits of nuclear power to the country as a whole and facts about the plant's benefit to the environment and the community.
- In recognition of a negative historical event. The opponents will issue many press releases on the anniversary of Chernobyl or Fukushima. Your activist organization can issue a press release about why that type of accident could not and did not happen at an American plant.
- Announcing that your group is holding a public meeting or a rally.
- Presenting your group's opinion on a local nuclear issue that is in the news. (This might be better as an op-ed than a press release. Or it could be a press release. It's a judgment call.)

Should you involve the plant?

IN MANY CASES, BUT NOT ALL, you might choose to share your plans and a draft of the press release with the public outreach people at your nuclear facility. They may be able to provide you with more information to use in your press release or other suggestions. If you plan a rally at the plant gates, for example, you must get the plant involved early. You may or may not be allowed to hold the rally, depending on many factors, including security issues. If you can hold the rally, you must include the plant in your planning.

On the other hand, if you are planning an event wholly sponsored by your group, I suggest that you do not get the nuclear facility involved. When we planned to rally on the streets of Brattleboro, Vermont Yankee management received the same press release, at the same time, as newspapers and media outlets received it. This was a rally sponsored by nuclear advocates, not by the people at Vermont Yankee. As it happened, the major plant union chose to send people to the rally and immediately contacted us. So you may end up getting support of some kind in your own rallies. Be sure that you only ask the plant for help when you want their help, not when you may get entangled with their permission process.

Union responded to press release. Michael Olson of Vermont Yankee IBEW, with pickup truck. At rally September 12, 2011. Being interviewed by Robbie Leppzer.

Basics of a press release

A BASIC PRESS RELEASE WILL include your organization's *one* media point of contact, a title, and the What, Who, When, Where and Why of the issue. You must have a single media point of contact for the press release. If reporters have follow-up questions, this will assure that your message is consistent throughout interviews.

Once you've established the topic of your press release, decide what information you want to include. Remember that most reporters are somewhat lazy (or maybe just overworked), and they will write their story directly from your press release. A savvy media person suggested that you should consider several positive messages you would want to read in the newspaper and include them in your press release.

Though it is important to have one *main* point to the press release, you should include auxiliary information. For example, a press release that announces a rally because the plant is back online after a refueling outage should, of course, announce the rally! It should tell when and where the rally will take place, who is sponsoring it, etc.

However, if possible, your press release can also include information on how much money the outage workers added to the local economy, what upgrades were done at the plant, and newly completed "Flex" modifications after Fukushima. This gives the reporters more to work with and increases the chances of positive coverage of your event.

Make sure you write clearly and simply. A press release is the place for simple thoughts or, at worst, complex thoughts expressed in simple sentences.

Exciting press releases: Catchy titles, cool quote

YOU CAN INCREASE THE INTEREST and effectiveness of your press release with catchy titles and great quotes.

Catchy titles: Grab the most positive, most interesting fact in your press release and use it for the title: "Know Nukes! Talk on Benefits of Nuclear Energy Sponsored by Granite Staters for Clean Air"; "US Nuclear Plants Not Like Fukushima, Says Nuclear Expert"; "Taxes and Schools and Nuclear Plants: Expert on Nuclear Plant Taxes Describes How Towns and States Benefit."

Quotes: You are an advocate, and you know other advocates. So you will have an easy time supplying another thing reporters love: a great quote. For your quote, you will need someone who has expertise but is not a plant employee. This person must give you permission to quote them in the press release. The quote should always support the information you're presenting in your press release.

You and the person being quoted should probably discuss the quote together. You suggest the topic you want them to cover, and they use their own unique words to cover it. This is the best kind of quotation situation: the quote isn't done in real time, so you have time to discuss it and get it right.

However, this is important: even when the two of you are happy with the quote, *always* give people you quote an opportunity to review the *entire* press release before it is distributed. Press releases are supposed to make friends, not enemies.

The boiler plate at the bottom

PROVIDE INFORMATION ABOUT YOUR organization at the bottom of your press release. For example, something like: "Granite Staters for Clean Air is a grassroots organization established to educate New Hampshire citizens on the clean air benefits of nuclear energy. New Hampshire is home to one nuclear power plant that powers millions of homes without generating harmful greenhouse gases. To learn more about our organization, please contact Jane Doe at 123-456-7890 or Doe@domain.org."

If your organization has a Facebook or Twitter account or website, you'll also want include the information at the bottom of the press release. For example: "Find Granite Staters for Clean air on Facebook at (your Facebook address)."

Distributing your press release

DISTRIBUTE YOUR PRESS RELEASE more or less the same way you send letters to the editor. Once again, Guy Page, former newspaper owner, reminds us that newspapers are very reluctant to open attachments. Send your press release in the body of the email, and in plain text, not HTML.

Address the email to yourself. Have your media contact list in the bcc field. You will usually send a press release to a larger list than the list you use for a letter to the editor. With a press release, you need to include TV and radio, too. In general, your press release media list should include the editor (or the generic newsroom address) at each newspaper, radio or TV station within approximately ten miles of the nuclear facility, as well as any other media who typically cover that facility.

You may receive media calls after distributing your press release. Be prepared to answer a few follow-up questions. If it is a radio reporter, they're probably only looking for a sound clip. Your press release may be too long to read on the radio, so you'll want to have an elevator speech at the ready. I discuss the elevator speech in chapter 20.

The bottom line

A PRESS RELEASE IS AN announcement. You basically say *what* the announcement is about and *who* is making the announcements. I think the guidelines in this chapter will help you write a good press release, right off the bat. There are also many websites devoted to "writing a good press release."

But don't sweat it too much. Have someone else read it, someone not in your group, so you can be sure you haven't said something that can be easily misinterpreted.

Beyond that, you have an advantage with any press release you distribute. The advantage is that you are "man bites dog." There are many anti-nuclear organizations distributing press releases endlessly. Because you are a pro-nuclear group, your press release will stand out from the crowd. So have fun, have a catchy title and a good quote . . . and you are on your way to fine publicity.

ACTION ITEM:

Find a template. Look up PRNewswire or other areas where press releases are distributed on the web. Do you see any examples you like? Print them as a template for your own press releases.[89]

CHAPTER TWENTY-FIVE

MEET THE PRESS!

PREVIOUS CHAPTERS DESCRIBED getting the word out to groups that are basically self-selected, and beginning to attend (and hopefully speak at) public meetings. Eventually, you may be talking to reporters, too. We have already started this topic with the basics of sending a press release.

The next stage of activism is being "out there" so many other people will learn that there are, indeed, people who favor nuclear energy. In other words, meeting the press (and meeting the radio, and even meeting TV).

There are many ways to be an activist. I consider it a smorgasbord of choices. Don't think you have to do it all.

Starting as an outsider

EVERY LITTLE BIT HELPS. You can't become a star of screen and TV, ducking paparazzi and so forth, all at once. So start small.

Here are some ways you might start.

With radio

ARE THERE SOME TALK SHOWS you listen to on the radio? Preferably, these will be local stations: don't aim for NPR. If you aren't "into" radio, ask your friends about which talk shows they listen to. The reason is that you can call into these shows when they are discussing energy and give a plug for nuclear energy. Local talk show hosts are eager for callers: they never get enough callers. The question is, what show to call?

The radio dials are crowded with shows, but only some are local, and only some are talk shows, and only some accept callers. And you aren't going to make a career of calling lots of shows: you just want to know about one or two shows you can call occasionally or regularly.

To some extent, the world of mainstream media (talk shows and so forth) is huge and unknowable. In another way, it is like a city. Nobody knows all the great restaurants in a city: most people know the restaurants in their neighborhood. Similarly, you can know (and call) a few local talk shows. These are the restaurants in your neighborhood.

When you begin calling shows (or later, when you are a guest on some shows) you will be pleasantly surprised at how many people remember hearing you. Most of us get a warm feeling when, over the radio or on the TV, we hear a voice: "Hey, it's someone I know! That is cool. Who would have thought it?" Your friends will get that feeling. In my opinion, being on local radio is one of the most satisfying parts of being an activist. Even people who disagree with you are likely to say something nice to you next time they see you, if they hear you on the radio.

Money and prestige and so forth, oh my!

ANOTHER QUESTION: How do you introduce yourself? If you didn't start or join a not-for-profit, I suggest that you file for a business name with your secretary of state. This is called a DBA, "Doing Business As." It is inexpensive and easy to do: the only hard part is looking online to be sure that the business name is not taken. It's very inexpensive to have a DBA: I believe mine costs about $50 for three years.

You don't have to use the DBA name very much, but when you move from being an outsider—when you move from calling the shows to being a guest on the shows—at that point, the person introducing you will want to say something about your affiliation. They will want to introduce you as "Meredith Angwin of the Energy Education Project" or "Meredith Angwin of Carnot Communications" (my DBA). You can also be introduced as "Meredith Angwin, with twenty-five years of experience in the utility industry." That is okay, too. I think it is good to be identified with a group or company, but it is not essential.

TV and video

IF YOU LOOK AT YOUR LOCAL TV listings, you will see that community TV stations broadcast many shows that are put together by ordinary people. They repeat these shows several times, and the shows are usually also available on the web. You may choose to have a show of this sort. Better yet (at least as you are getting started), look at some of the existing shows and volunteer to be interviewed on them. You have to choose your shows, of course. *Fine Cooking in Our Town* probably doesn't want to interview you. But other shows may well choose do so.

If you do put a show together, the community TV station will almost certainly supply you with a bare bones set (you might want to bring your own signature backdrop, which you can make with a friend) and will record the show. Your expenditure will be very little or nothing.

Video is straightforward, also. It takes little preparation to put up a YouTube channel. However, most of those YouTube channels never get many followers, and I suggest that making an occasional video (if you want to) for your blog would be a better choice. If you want to be on video, I suggest that you choose community TV. First, you will be on TV. People will see you. Second, you may be able to put the episode up on Vimeo, if your community TV station has not already done that.

One problem with making your own videos is that it can be a trap, a true time sink. There are lovely programs for editing videos: don't you want to edit it? No, actually, you don't. If you have self-control, you can improve your video with twenty minutes of editing. If you don't have self-control, you will be working at it for hours. These are hours you could have spent talking to people, writing letters to the editor, or skiing. You only have a certain number of hours available in each day: don't spend them editing videos, unless you enjoy editing videos.

On the other hand, a friend of mine who makes a fair number of videos says that the usual problem is that people don't prepare a good enough script before making the video. A good script can save a great deal of editing time. My friend makes excellent videos, so he should know. With or without a script, making videos is a skill, and it takes time to acquire this skill. You have to decide if the result is worth the work.

Edging toward insider status: Helping a reporter out

THERE'S A WEBSITE CALLED Help a Reporter Out, in which you sign up to be notified if a reporter needs to speak with someone with a specific background.[90] At one point, I signed up to be a "source," but I rarely found a request for my expertise. The science reporting they list is usually health reporting. When they want a "science expert," they often want a nutrition expert. However, their concept is great.

If you can, you should help a reporter out.

Remember, though, that the whole relationship with reporters is more of a courtship than an assault. Buttonholing a reporter at a meeting will not get you appreciated or quoted . . . unless the reporter knows you ahead of time and you have something useful to say. This is another situation in which a blog is very useful: the reporters will read authoritative blogs that cover their beat. Then, when you meet the reporters, they may not quote you, but they will at least say hello.

When a reporter writes a good story, thank her in a brief email. Don't simultaneously criticize the story (that is my opinion, anyway); just say something in the story that you felt was well explained or well stated. If the reporter makes a factual mistake in a story, also write a brief note explaining the correct facts and noting that you are available for questions, any time.

Sometimes, when you already have a tentative relationship with a reporter, you can email her before some anniversary.

For example, before March 11, you can write the reporter and note that nobody died of radiation at Fukushima, and the latest report from the WHO says that excess cancers are not expected. Say you are happy to be quoted, and include your phone number so that she can call you for a quote. She may. She may not. As I said, it's a courtship.

Eventually, you may get calls from reporters when something happens and they want the opinion of people on both sides of the issue. You have something valuable to offer the reporters, and it is not what you think it is. You know that your assessments are fact-based, not fear-based. You think this is important. Some reporters may value this; many will not.

The reporter is after both sides of the story, and by its nature, the plant is going to give rather bland answers. That is what you have to offer. You may be able to give more colorful (but still accurate) answers, and that can be very helpful. You are a more colorful "she said" than the plant will give.

You don't have to wait for an event to meet with a reporter. You can call a reporter, announce your new group, and meet with her for lunch or coffee as a getting-to-know-you event. You want to show yourself as someone who has expertise and can speak clearly on the subject, and as someone who is accessible to answer a question or give a quote. (After all, that is who you are.) If you have an upcoming event, be sure to mention that you will be sending out a press release soon.

The one thing you should *not* do is attempt to buy the reporter lunch. Oh, you might say "can I pick this up?" when the check comes. That's almost an instinct for some of us. However, the reporter's answer is sure to be "no." Journalistic ethics prevent reporters from taking any type of favor or gift from the people they interview.

Your sound bites

THE OPPONENTS ARE EXCELLENT at giving memorable answers. The answers may not be accurate, but they are memorable. One of the hall of fame moments, for me, was when an opponent said that a nuclear company was either "devious or dumb." You have to hand it to him: that has a ring to it.

However, nuclear supporters can also use clever sound bites. The problem is that we don't take a few minutes ahead of the interview to think up some sound bites. Some sound-bite pointers:

- Brevity is good.
- Alliteration is memorable.
- Opposition is memorable: "devious or dumb."

Here are some pro-nuclear sound bites, but you should make up your own sound bites for your own occasion.

- It's nuclear or fracking.
- Split, don't emit.
- Nice rhetoric, lousy physics.

If you have facts, are willing to state the facts in amusing and memorable ways, and are available but not terribly pushy, reporters will ultimately call you and interview you. Sometimes for print, sometimes for radio, sometimes even for TV. Community TV stations may ask you to be on the program.

Choose and enjoy

FROM THE GREAT SMORGASBORD of possible activities, you will have picked some visible activities and had some fun. Now it is time to think about how to find places to speak.

ACTION ITEM:

Airwaves. Listen to radio or ask your friends. Which local radio talk shows would you like to be on?

WHITE PAPER 5

NUCLEAR ENERGY AROUND THE WORLD

WORLDWIDE, DEMAND FOR ENERGY is growing. The International Energy Agency estimates that world energy use will close to double by 2040 compared to 2010. The developed countries (OECD countries) will use about the same amount of energy thirty years from now as they do now. Meanwhile, the non-OECD countries will basically double their energy use.[91]

The worldwide need for energy

THE WORLDWIDE NEED FOR ENERGY explains why there is a worldwide boom in nuclear energy.

According to the World Nuclear Association, approximately 160 new nuclear plants are planned to come online within the next ten years—and they're needed. In addition to global growth in energy use, the US and Europe are seeing the need to replace aging generators, especially considering that carbon emission standards are becoming tighter. An increased awareness of climate change is also leading the public and decision-makers to agree that the use of fossil fuels must be reduced. Though the COP21 agreement adopted in Paris[92] will probably be ineffective (in my opinion), it did show some willingness to at least talk about curtailing the use of fossil fuels.[93]

But there is another aspect to the energy boom. As people leave poverty, they use more electricity. They become more like people in developed countries.

In developed countries, people are generally healthy. They have long life expectancies, healthy babies, small families, and education for all. They also have an abundance of reliable electricity. These things go together.

Energy and women's lives

DEVELOPING COUNTRIES HAVE low life expectancies, low education (especially among women), and high infant mortality. Many of the people in these countries do not have electricity. The *Washington Post* has a great infographic titled "Without electricity, 1.3 billion are living in the dark" that illustrates the countries in which people don't have access to electricity.[94]

More than 600 million people in sub-Saharan Africa, and more than 300 million in India, are living without access to electricity.[95]

As people leave poverty, their lives get better. Especially as women leave poverty, their lives get better. They have fewer children and more education. Robert Hargraves made a splendid graph of this called "Prosperity versus Birth Rate." It is in his book *Thorium, Energy Cheaper Than Coal* and reprinted on my blog.[96]

For more on the interaction between women and energy, I recommend the video of the "Magic Washing Machine," by Hans Rosling. Rosling argues that the washing machine was one of the most important inventions in world history, because of its effect on women's lives.[97]

As a matter of fact, I get annoyed when renewable advocates explain that we can use more electricity in off-hours, for example, by doing wash when the wind blows at night and there is low demand on the grid. Exactly who do they expect will be up late at night, when ordinary demand on the grid is down, and now it's time to do the wash? I wrote about this in "The Oversold Smart Grid: Dismissing the Work of Women."[98]

Despite the hype about renewables, the developing countries of the world will use fossil or nuclear to bring their people out of poverty. The International Energy Agency (IEA) projects worldwide growth in the use of coal, gas, and oil, as well as nuclear. I wish I could say the nuclear portion was growing faster than the coal portion, but it doesn't seem to be. But at least the nuclear portion is growing.[99] There are sixty reactors under construction in about fourteen countries, and many other nuclear plants are being upgraded to produce more power.[100]

Electricity and the end of poverty mean that everybody has a better life. The only way to do this without extensive use of fossil fuels is through nuclear energy. To a large extent, energy is a main source of any "liberation" women have, whether it is their ability to go to school, or have safe drinking water, refrigeration, and a decent cook stove that doesn't put pollutants into the family living space.

I support nuclear energy so that people (especially women) can lead safe and productive lives. It's a moral issue, a feminist issue, and a personal issue. Nuclear energy is clean, safe, and abundant. Nuclear energy is the Power to Save the World.

CHAPTER TWENTY-SIX

FINDING PLACES
TO SPEAK

FINDING PLACES TO SPEAK is a smorgasbord of its own. There are many choices. This chapter is about speaking to local community groups.

There are two types of places to speak:

- Places you arrange
- Places arranged by some group

Of these two, the places arranged by some group (Rotary, church, political party) are far superior, in my opinion. These groups know that they will get an audience. They have the infrastructure in place to hold the meeting. All you have to do is get on the agenda and show up. Oh, if you are giving a presentation using PowerPoint, you also need to figure out what equipment they have, and what equipment you will have to bring. But, basically, all you have to do is show up ready to talk.

221

Places you arrange

IF YOU WANT TO ARRANGE a meeting on your own, there are a few things you need to think about. First, will it be open to the public? Will it be listed in the newspaper?

Public meetings

MOST PLACES THAT HAVE meeting rooms (your local science museum, libraries) sometimes say that all "community meetings" held in those rooms must be open to the public. This can be excellent: somebody pro-nuclear can see the meeting announcement in the paper and attend. On the other hand, someone anti-nuclear (or a bunch of them) can also attend. I have held two meetings, open to the public, which anti-nuclear people attended. I have to say that at our meetings, even the anti-nuclear people were very polite. I allowed them to put their flyers on our table, along with our own flyers. So there were "facts about radiation" flyers of all kinds on the table.

A meeting that you host will probably not be covered extensively in the press, unlike a hearing of some type. Therefore, the most impolite anti-nuclear people probably won't bother to attend your meeting. On the other hand, when I thought about having a pro-nuclear open meeting in Brattleboro (home to people who shout, threaten, and throw manure), a friend who lives in Brattleboro urged me not to do so. She said that security issues for such a meeting would just be too difficult in that town. And possibly too expensive.

So you have to figure out your own local situation about holding an open meeting.

Who is hosting

WHO IS HOSTING THE MEETING? You don't want to advertise something like, "Meredith Angwin is holding a meeting." This is where your small company or organization, or the American Nuclear Society, or Women in Nuclear, or your local college's nuclear program (if they have one) becomes very useful. Use your group name—for example, "Energy Education Project is hosting a meeting"—and see how many cosponsors (other groups) can be listed on the announcement. You want to have legitimacy (more groups, more legitimacy) and get some press. Also, more groups mean more people to bring cookies. Never forget the cookies!

Speaking of getting some press: send an email to your media list about the meeting. Some reporters may choose to cover the meeting, and, hopefully, some radio hosts will announce it. You may be asked to be on the radio to talk about the upcoming meeting. If you are going to have a public meeting, don't fly under the radar. Put announcements in the local paper, send out some kind of press release, or whatever will help.

Private meetings

MY FEELING IS THAT YOU SHOULD plan two private meetings for every public meeting. These are meetings, not necessarily big ones, to which you invite your supporters, to do some planning or to hear a speaker. These can be in your home, someone else's home, or in a place you rent. The "rent" business is because the free places (libraries and schools) generally want to host public meetings as part of their public service.

I admit it: I have not done that many private meetings. I did one that was very successful: it was a dinner at a hotel, only supporters invited, not the press. Under these circumstances, I was able to get a speaker panel that included (for example) a utility executive and a man who writes many opinion pieces but seldom appears on the public stage. Though I was worried about the cost, I told people it was free but they were welcome to contribute to the project. These were supporters of the Energy Education Project, so, as you can guess, they contributed so much that the project made money on the dinner. I suppose it is only one step from this to a real fundraiser dinner.

Citizens for Nuclear Technology Awareness, a pro-nuclear association in Savannah, Georgia, has many fundraising breakfasts with guest speakers, "Up and Atom Breakfasts."[101]

Remember the smorgasbord concept. These things are all choices, and many of them can be very effective. You can't do them all, but don't dismiss private meetings just because they are not public. Private meetings can be very supportive, and your people will be energized both by the program and by the support of other people at the meeting. Being among friends is always a good thing.

Meetings someone else arranges

MANY GROUPS HAVE REGULARLY scheduled meetings and want to have interesting and possibly controversial speakers. The advantage of such talks is that the place is pre-arranged, the audience is pre-arranged, and all you have to do is give the talk. Another advantage is that you speak to people who might not care all that much about energy issues. They might not come to a talk advertised as being about energy issues, but they come to this group regularly, and sometimes they hear about healthcare and sometimes about living a spiritual life and sometimes . . . they hear *you*, and you find new people who have interest in a good energy policy.

SIGN-UP SHEET

YEAH: *SIGN-UP SHEET IS IN ALL CAPS*, because I am shouting! It drives me completely nuts that people go and give a talk, and they don't have a sign-up sheet ready to pass around. I mean READY: clipboard or hard backing, pen, place for a name, and place for an email address. Get this going early, as soon as you begin to speak or even sooner, because people scribble their email addresses, and you or your friend will have to check them for legibility, or you will lose access to a person who wanted to opt in to follow your project. Don't let that happen.

Finding the public meetings

START WITH THE GROUPS you belong to, or that other people belong to. A short list includes Rotary, Kiwanis, chambers of commerce, Lions Clubs, Optimist Societies, fraternal societies (Elks, for example), retirement communities and political groups (Republican, Democrat, Libertarian, Progressive, Tea Party, socialist, League of Women Voters). Religious organizations, including churches, synagogues, mosques. Hindu temples, pagan groups and atheist groups. Veteran's groups. Local sections of engineering societies such as ASME. The list goes on. Many groups have regular meetings, and many of them want speakers.

To see the types of meetings available, I can look at my alumni bulletin from the University of Chicago physical sciences department. They write about David Archer, a geophysics professor who speaks about climate change. He has spoken at "churches, atheist meetings, libraries, physics departments at other universities, retirement communities, and even Chicago's . . . wastewater treatment plant."[102]

(Note: if you have someone with a Ph.D. in physical sciences in your group, you may well be able to have him or her give a seminar at a neighboring college or law school.)

The question isn't even *finding* these meetings: it is picking them and getting on the agenda. As in many of these chapters, this could be a book in itself, and maybe I will write that book one of these days.

Meanwhile, here are some thoughts:

- Have someone in your group who is *not* the designated speaker arrange the events. This is because the speaker will be busy enough, and also the speaker can't boast for herself very effectively. Imagine the scenario where the speaker calls up and says, "Hey, I am tremendously knowledgeable about nuclear energy. I have been giving quite a few talks, and I would like to talk to your group." This is not as good as the scenario where Joe calls up and says, "Hey, we have someone in our group who is tremendously knowledgeable about nuclear energy and has been giving quite a few talks; and she is so busy that I have offered to do some scheduling for her. Would you be interested in a talk on this topic?" The second scenario is much better.

- Start with Rotaries. There are many Rotaries in any area, and they have a speaker every single week. Every week. Also, the Rotaries in a given area have some sort of master list (talk to someone in your group who belongs to Rotary) so that you can call the different people who arrange the speakers. So this is an easy place to start. Another reason to start here is that you probably won't actually end up giving your first talk at a Rotary. They tend to be very popular with speakers, and they schedule months in advance. That can be a drawback, or it can be . . . another reason why Rotary is an easy place to start.

- Don't forget the groups that are your natural allies: engineering organizations, physics departments, and so forth. They are more willing to help you.

- Unions. Nuclear power plants are generally union shops, with strong membership for IBEW and sometimes the pipefitters union. If you speak at one of the union meetings, as one of our friends in California did, you can expect support and many sign-ups on the sign-up sheets. Union members are frequently willing to be very active supporters of nuclear power because they see it close up. They know they are supporting clean power and good employment for union members.

- For the rest, all I can say is, be open. With some groups (Rotary) you end up going through the scheduling person. With many groups, you just need to know someone in the group and talk to that person. Be willing to speak at community college events and so forth. Speak at your own place of worship: they may well have an "adult ed" program on community topics, and be looking for speakers.

- Youth, political and so forth. You will be invited, perhaps, to Republican, Tea Party, and Libertarian groups. Try to get invited by the other side, also. The talk may not be as pleasant an experience as talking to people who mostly already agree with you, but don't assume that all people in the opposite party disagree with you. It is harder to get on the agenda at schools, but sometimes a school has an Energy Unit and some student will contact you. Follow up. Don't just talk to the students; ask if you can call the teacher and volunteer to address the class. This sounds as if it could take all your time, but my own experience is that opportunities at schools happen so rarely that it will not take all your time.

- There's a Nuclear Science Week every year, with a website and many pre-arranged activities that you can adapt.[103] The local nuclear company (with some suggestions, perhaps, from you) may participate in Nuclear Science Week in a local school.

- Speaking of schools, in my opinion, all nuclear facilities should encourage their employees to speak at Career

Days at their children's school, and at any other school having a Career Day.

- If you have a local chapter of ANS, Women in Nuclear, or other pro-nuclear organization, see if you can trade venue searches with them. Where have they spoken that you can speak? Where have you spoken that they can speak?

Never forget: this is part of a smorgasbord, not a requirement. You do what you can, you choose what you do, and every little bit helps.

ACTION ITEM:

Where could you speak? Find two places you might speak. Think about groups you might speak to, and investigate how they choose their speakers. You don't have to actually speak. Just look into it. If they beg you to speak while you are just investigating (this definitely happens), remember that you can always say "no."

CHAPTER TWENTY-SEVEN

PRESENTING AT A MEETING: THE SLIDE SHOW

REMEMBERING THAT THIS IS smorgasbord, not a set of rules or must-do's, this chapter will explore preparing a slide show.

Preparing a talk or slide show

FOR MANY MEETINGS, IT IS good to have a slide show prepared and ready to show. For other meetings, it isn't a good idea. There is a certain amount of overhead in slide shows, beyond the time you need to prepare the show. You have to be sure they are set up for slide shows, or you must bring your own set-up. Then you have to set it up.

So, the first question is: Do you want to bring a slide show? Or do you want to give a talk without visual aids?

And the next question after that is: Is the venue set up for slide shows?

My advice is that if it is a short meeting (breakfast group with speakers, for example) and they are not set up for slide shows—don't bother. Bringing lots of equipment (projector, adapter for computer, screen) is just too much overhead for you. Just speak.

On the other hand, if they are set up for slide shows, you may find that giving a short slide show is very effective. Most people retain visual information better than spoken information, and most people are accustomed to presentations with colorful slides. So, *if* the venue is set up for slide shows, I recommend you do a slide show. It will still be more overhead, because even if they are set up, you will probably need to bring a computer, and possibly an adapter to fit your computer (if it is an Apple) with their visual feed. In my opinion, however, this is worthwhile.

Including visual information is a major reason that a slide show is better for the audience. The slides keep people's attention and are more easily remembered than a string of statements.

However, a slide show can also be helpful for you. It is reassuring. There are your slides up on the screen, your old familiar slides that you know so well. Seeing them is reassuring, and you feel that you are prepared. Stage fright fades, to some extent, because . . . there they are, looking just the way you remember them. The slides look good, and you aren't going to get nervous and lose your place in the talk because the slides keep you on track.

Now that you have decided on slides/not slides, how do you put the talk together? It's the old method of tell them what you are going to tell them, tell them, then tell them what you told them. Don't make the beginner's mistake of trying to rush through all sorts of material that you think is *so* important you must tell it all. In a twenty-minute talk, you can make only three points. To some extent, you can make only one point, but three is more interesting. Are you going to leave stuff out? Well, yes you are. You are going to leave lots of stuff out. Yes, even important stuff! And you know what . . . that is what the question period is for.

A couple of hacks on this. (Nowadays, people seem to be calling every hint a "hack." I just read a recipe that included "hacks for your slow cooker." If you can "hack" a slow cooker, you can "hack" anything.)

First, if your total time is twenty minutes (as it is at many Rotaries), do not plan to talk for more than ten minutes. If your time is thirty minutes, don't go a minute over twenty in your main talk, maybe not over fifteen. Leave as much time for questions as you can manage. Do not believe you have to force-feed facts to the audience. The question period is where the audience interacts with you. The question period is when the audience is more interested, more engaged, and will remember more.

Second: bring extra slides. Are there four issues you don't have time for but you wish you could talk about? Bring four slides, and put those slides *after* your final wrap-up slide, perhaps separated by a slide saying "extra topics." Then, when you get the questions, you will be prepared again. Your slides will be helpful to the questioner and reassuring to you. Do not bring more than one slide on each topic. You are answering questions, not giving another talk.

Third hack (and maybe this deserves the title of "hack"): bring your slides two ways. Don't assume that just because your slides work on your computer, and you have all the right adapters, that everything is going to work. I also bring a thumb drive with the presentation on it so I can put it on the projector through some other computer if necessary. (I know. This is obvious. It's obvious right up to the day you forget to bring the thumb drive, there's a projector problem with your computer, and half your speaking time is taken up with issues of getting it to work.)

Preparing the talk (or slide show) itself

FIRST OF ALL, HOW TO organize it. There are books on this, but let's be honest.

PowerPoint templates are pretty good. You know: title slide, list of points, point one, backup one, point two, backup two, etc. Also, remember Point of View Plus Two from chapter 22.

Yes, I understand Edward Tufte's[104] point about the visual communication of scientific data. His main book is terrific: *The Visual Display of Quantitative Information.*[105]

However, I don't agree with Tufte's criticisms of PowerPoint. I have a lot of communication-oriented friends who are also Tufte fans who will be all over me about this. All annoyed and everything. They will say, "PowerPoint is boring! PowerPoint is evil. I can't believe you wrote this."

Well. I wrote it. PowerPoint is popular because it is a good hack. It leads you to a very acceptable progression for your presentation. So, choose your points and your PowerPoint template and go for it.

You can also use PowerPoint formats for a verbal presentation, except that it is easier. You make the outline, but you don't have to make the slides themselves. See chapter 21 on making a public statement for why it is often better to speak from a list of points rather than read a written talk aloud.

A personal slide show

MAKE THE SLIDE SHOW personal if you possibly can. When the nuclear opponent says, "I'm scared," everyone has automatic empathy because everyone has been scared.

When the nuclear supporter says, "Science shows us . . ."— nobody has empathy with that.

Nuclear proponents often come across as overbearing and condescending because they are so busy giving the scientific reasons for being in favor of nuclear energy, and they leave out their own feelings and their own story. You don't have to be Garrison Keillor, but don't be afraid to tell a relevant story from your own life or include some humor. You are not wasting the audience's time by doing this: you are connecting with the audience.

Pro-nuclear people are fact-oriented. We want to get the facts out there. However, what people remember from a presentation is stories. Try to include a relevant story, or put some facts in terms of a story.

For example, when talking about how nuclear energy contributes to cleaner air, you could tell the story of how the Asthma Association of Canada testified in favor of keeping nuclear plants operating. That is memorable: statistics are far less memorable. Yes, include the statistics, but try to also include a story, too. A video of the Asthma Association of Canada testimony is available on my blog. The section I am referring to begins at 5:50 (5 minutes, 50 seconds).[106]

So, the next question: what is a story? Basically, it has people as the actors, not numbers. That's all. You don't have to become a raconteur.

Also, you will hear the advice, "Don't read your slides aloud." Sometimes people take this advice too far and are careful to *not* read the words on the slides, but instead say other things about the same area or topic. Frankly, when I am in the audience, this drives me crazy. I always have to concentrate pretty hard to follow a verbal exposition. If the verbal exposition is going along and there's a slide up there saying something related but not quite the same . . . I get to the point of wanting to throw something. If I read the slide, I will miss a sentence of the verbal exposition and vice versa. And yet, the advice is right. Don't read the slide.

That is, don't read it directly. Let's say there are three short sentences on the slide. Don't start by reading the three sentences aloud, as if the audience needs help in order to read. Read the first sentence, and then go on to explain it a bit, offer an example, or whatever. Then read the second sentence. *Merge* the verbal and the visual as you speak. Make it easy for the audience.

If the slide is mostly a graph or a picture, name it: "This graph shows the relationship between electricity prices and natural gas prices on the New England grid." Then talk about it more and explain it.

More hints for the show

WHICH BRINGS US another problem with Tufte. He is fond of very dense information on a slide. He often uses the example of this graph of Napoleon's armies marching to Russia.[107]

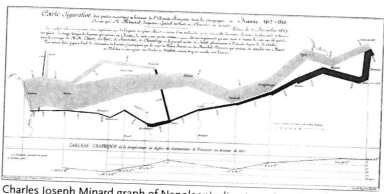

Charles Joseph Minard graph of Napoleon's disastrous invasion of Russia, including information on number of troops, temperatures, distances, dates, and more. Credit: Wikipedia https://en.wikipedia.org/wiki/Charles_Joseph_Minard

This is indeed a dense illustration. It contains the size of the army, and how its size diminished over time (there's a time scale). It shows how far the army marched each day (a distance scale). They marched in freezing conditions (there's a temperature scale). When they crossed a major river, the river appears on the graph. Considering the huge amount of information this graph contains, it is a masterwork.

However, if you make a slide this dense with information, everyone is going to hate it and nobody is going to get much out of it. The way you can read and contemplate while holding a well-illustrated book is quite different from watching a slide in a relatively fast presentation. That's true even if the speaker spends lots of time on "this is the time scale and this is the distance scale and this is . . . etc." You just can't get that much out of a single slide on a screen.

For your own presentation, each graphic slide (like each slide with just words) needs to be one point and one point only. That is as much as people can grasp in a presentation.

Tritium: How Dangerous?

- Beta radiation (electrons)
- Potassium is also beta emitter
- 2 quarts of EPA limit water = 1/20th of a banana

A slide I have used to put tritium in perspective: one point only

And don't speed-talk. We all want to say so much, but speed-talk is not effective. Budget one minute per slide for the presentation. A friend of mine had an hour to talk, including the question period, and he originally put together about 70 slides. I jumped on him about that and he cut down the number. He didn't cut it enough, in my opinion. Thirty slides would have been much better. Remember, it's not about how much you *know*, it's about how much you can *effectively communicate*. Also, the audience is truly engaged during the question period. The question period is when true two-way communication takes place. Leave time for questions.

In your presentation, just move to the next slide in a straightforward way. Don't do fancy dissolves and so forth: they are just distracting. PowerPoint allows you to do some rather silly things, in my opinion. Don't do them.

About the slides themselves: it is not hard to use PowerPoint, but if you want some expert help, get it. Either from a professional or from a friend.

Put your name on each slide, in small print.

What about slide backup? You should have references for any factual assertion you make, but it is impossible to put references on the slides themselves without being distracting. One man I know puts references on his website. Another possibility is to make a "slide" of a list of references for all the other slides. Sort of like endnotes in a book. You don't show that slide, but it is there for the question period. And if someone wants a hard copy of your slides, they get the endnote slide (or slides) also.

As for the rest: practice with a friend before presenting (concentrate on getting the timing right) and then . . . learn by doing. That's all.

TWENTY-EIGHT

THE FRIENDLY PRESENTATION

THE LAST CHAPTER WAS MOSTLY about the slides. But it is not just about the slides. Your presentation must be friendly. You want to invite the audience to care about the presentation, to be interested in the slides, and to ask questions. (**Note:** I used to hide behind my slides. From personal experience, I can tell you that Eugene Grecheck's advice is really important—see below.)

Look at your audience

IT IS TREMENDOUSLY EASY to hide behind your slides. Look up, at least some of the time. Look at your audience.

As Eugene Grecheck, past president of the American Nuclear Society, retired vice president for Nuclear Engineering and Development at Dominion Nuclear, and experienced speaker, said, "Try to connect with individuals in the crowd who are genuinely there out of interest in the topic. That means understanding what their concerns may be, and then speaking as a fellow human being directly to them. When standing in front of the group, look people in the eye and speak to them as people, not a crowd. I have found that if you do this successfully, even adamant zealots find themselves at least listening. I've had some come up to me later and tell me that I was the first industry person they ever met that they felt was speaking from the heart, and not just a script. They still didn't agree with me, but they did at least admit that I was a real person."

Have a handout

FACTS ARE IMPORTANT, but people remember stories. What to do?

You should have facts in your presentation, but you don't want to get so bogged down with facts that you can't tell the memorable stories.

The answer is the handout. Have a one-pager on the table, with some of your points and some references. When answering questions, you can refer people to the handout. You can suggest that they take it home and look up what you said.

Make sure your handouts are scrupulously accurate. Nothing can ever be complete (someone will undoubtedly want to know something that is not on your handout), but what is on your handout must be accurate.

Traveling with a friend

IT IS TRULY TERRIFIC IF A friend will come with you to the presentation. He or she can help you set up and generally be a reassuring presence.

The friend can be in the audience, or the friend can be on the stage with you. Two-part presentations can be very effective.

In one case, Patty O'Donnell, business owner and former state representative for Vernon, the town with Vermont Yankee, gave a series of presentations at clubs and Rotaries. Her research (and many people's research) had shown that people who work at the plant are the most credible speakers on plant operation and safety. The people in the audience know that the plant people *absolutely* know what they are talking about. And people in the audience realize they can ask questions of the plant person, and the questions will be answered.

At least ten people from Vermont Yankee volunteered to help O'Donnell. O'Donnell set up the meetings and introduced the Vermont Yankee workers. She made it very clear that the plant folks were there as volunteers, on their own time, and speaking from their knowledge. They were not paid and they were not acting as official plant representatives.

O'Donnell often started with a very short presentation about Vermont Yankee on the grid and the plant's economic benefits. Then she gave the podium to the man or woman from the plant. The plant worker gave a presentation on safety at Vermont Yankee. O'Donnell and the plant employee both answered questions. This was very effective.

Similarly, Howard Shaffer and I gave two talks about being pro-nuclear activists, both at ANS meetings. We each did some of the slides, and we traded off talking. He spoke about presenting to government groups, and I spoke about blogging and writing letters. This was also very effective.

With a two-person presentation, you must each have a clearly defined expertise for the presentation (even if, in practice, your expertise areas overlap). This gives the audience a clear idea of why there are two presenters, and which person is likely to answer which kind of question.

Also, only do a two-person presentation when your presentation time is at least thirty minutes. Two people attempting to present within a fifteen-minute window will just be choppy and hard to follow.

I do not mean to imply that this two-person show is what you should do. But I want to point out that you have a smorgasbord of choices, and the two-person presentation is a very enjoyable choice.

In a debate

I DO NOT WANT TO GET TOO FAR into the subject of "how to debate nuclear opponents" because that is truly Advanced Activism, and I want people to feel capable of activism, not intimidated by it. But, if you have a chance to get in front of an audience to debate, remember that a debate is just a short presentation (your presentation) followed by the other presentation, and then you ask each other questions or answer questions. It can be pretty stressful as you prepare, but debates are rarely more than an hour long, so it flies by quickly. Once you have your own presentation together (twenty minutes), you are basically prepared for a debate. Also, if you look up your opponent's earlier talks, you can see what he usually says. With a little work, you can be prepared for your rebuttal, before you even see the opponent face-to-face.

I must emphasize: don't debate unless there is a strong moderator. Your opponent is probably more expert than you at holding the floor. After your initial presentation, which may be scheduled for only ten minutes or so, if there isn't a strong moderator, you may not be able to get a word in edgewise.

If you find yourself in that sort of situation, however, debating without a strong moderator, you must just call your debate opponent on his or her rudeness. "Excuse me, but I need to finish that sentence." "Please don't interrupt." "Let me finish without jumping in, please. You will have your turn." In case you are wondering: no, this isn't much fun. Far better to have a strong moderator.

ACTION ITEM:

Consider effectiveness. Next time you hear a presentation, take note of what works and what doesn't. Maybe take actual notes, not of the subject matter, but of the effectiveness of the presentation.

CHAPTER TWENTY-NINE

LEGISLATIVE COMMITTEES

FIRST, I WANT TO DISTINGUISH this chapter from chapter 23. That chapter is about hearings, and about speaking in public, in a situation that calls for public comment. A hearing usually takes place in a large room (the public is invited), and people line up or sign up for a chance to speak.

This chapter is about speaking in a smaller group, in a legislative committee. In general, such committee meetings are open to the public (due to various sunshine laws), but the public is rarely invited to comment to the committee. To speak before such a committee, you have to be invited to do so. In general, this invitation will only come if

- You have some credentials to speak
- You solicit the invitation by telling someone who can invite you that you want to speak

Obviously, this is advanced-smorgasbord in terms of activism and will not be something everyone can or will do. However, my experience is that ordinary people think that such an opportunity is basically impossible to achieve, and it isn't. So first, let's talk about how you would get to speak before the committee.

Credentials

YOU NEED TO HAVE SOME credentials.

I need to tell you that the bar is not high here. Anti-nuclear activists, with flimsy credentials, regularly speak to such committees. You may be thinking, "I am not an expert." So what? Anti-nuclear people who dropped out of college testify before legislative committees.[108]

Instead of thinking, "I am not an expert," which is a becomingly modest statement for a private person, think, "Do I or does someone in my group have credentials that could move us in front of this committee?" That's the activist statement.

Credentials can be
- Having a degree in science or engineering
- Being an executive or staff or member of the board of directors in a small not-for-profit that is pro-nuclear
- Having worked at a nuclear plant or other nuclear facility
- Holding a PE (professional engineering) license
- Being an executive or staff or on the board of directors in a not-for-profit that is in favor of clean air, such as the asthma association (testified in Canada)[109]
- Having written a book about anything in science or public policy, but especially about nuclear or climate or energy

- Having written articles about anything in science or public policy, but especially about nuclear or climate or energy
- Being a professor (of pretty much anything, with the possible exception of medieval literature)
- Having a Ph.D. (in pretty much anything, as above). For example, one man with a Ph.D. in sociology has testified and written books against nuclear energy, while letting people think that his Ph.D. is in economics
- Having been an energy regulator (state or federal) or member of the staff of EPA, at any level
- Testifying before another committee, or at an administrative hearing
- Previous qualification as an expert witness in litigation (see below)
- Also, identifying with a professional society, such as the American Nuclear Society or another engineering society, will add to your credibility.

As you can see, it is not that high a bar. Someone in your group (probably several people) is qualified to make statements in front of a legislative body.

A note about being a professional engineer. If you are an engineer, you may have stronger criteria in the back of your mind. To give certain types of advice about engineering projects, especially government engineering projects, you need to be a registered Professional Engineer in that state, with your credentials up to date. There are similar rules about being an expert witness in a court case. That is the sort of thing that most engineers think about when they think about stepping in front of a government body.

If someone in the group has been qualified as an expert witness in litigation, be sure to describe this qualification when the person asks to speak in front of a legislative committee. The bar for "expert witness" is pretty high, and once you are qualified as an expert by one court, other courts will almost certainly admit you to speak on similar topics. Similarly, legislative committees are very likely to accept the person's credentials.

In many cases, you also need to have credentials of this sort to speak to semi-judicial bodies, such as public service boards and public utility commissions. In these hearings, the list of those who will testify is presented early in the hearing, and usually the resumes (at least on the pro-nuclear side) are quite long and carefully put together.

I am sorry to say, but I have to say, that after watching various anti-nuclear people say their piece to Vermont legislative committees, I realized some differences. Actual engineering projects and expert witness assignments require real expertise and credentials. For speaking to a legislature, only rather thin credentials are required. Getting in front of the legislature is more about publicity and showmanship than credentials, at least for the nuclear opponents. Instead of being annoyed at this fact, look at it as liberating. If they can speak to the committee, so can you!

So, now that you know that you *can* speak to the committee, how do you get to do so?

The legislative two-step

THERE ARE TWO STEPS to speaking in front of a legislative committee.

The first step is to know which committees are concerned with energy, and when they will be considering bills or advisory statements.

The second step is being invited to speak to them on those occasions.

Finding the hearing

TO SOME EXTENT, THE FIRST STEP is the hardest. Many legislatures post committee meetings and bills they are considering, but it can be a full-time job to follow this on the web. (Okay, not full time, but it certainly takes more time than is pleasant to read lists of meeting times.) The best is if you can get a heads-up. For example, if the plant has a friend in the legislature, someone who always stands up for the plant, befriend that person; at least, be friendly enough to ask if they can give you a heads-up about when the committee will be talking about energy or nuclear.

Another possibility is that you get to know the people (shocking, I know) who are lobbyists for your plant. And ask them for a heads-up, etc. Some legislatures have specialty newspapers (often on the web) that cover their actions more thoroughly than the general press. These might also be helpful. The hardest thing may be finding out when you want to show up. In some cases, the legislation may be so high profile that it is easy to hear about the meetings. In other cases, you have to follow the committee pretty closely to know what is happening.

In any case, let us say that there is a legislative hearing on how the local power plant is hurting the fish or nuclear fuel rods should have a special tax or whatever. You have learned about it, and you plan to be there.

Being invited to speak

BEING INVITED IS NOT AS HARD as it might seem. Let us assume that the nuclear opponents have invited a speaker or a couple of speakers. The person who has to issue the invitation is the committee chairperson. Let us assume that the committee chairperson is a nuclear opponent, and he has enjoyed inviting the anti-nuclear speakers.

You can probably still be invited to speak. You have to find the ranking member on the committee. This person is a member of the committee, and he is the person of the highest rank in the opposition party. He is, to some extent, the "shadow chairman." Everyone knows that, come the next election, if the party balance changes in the legislature, the committee chairmen will be from the winning party, the dominant party. Neither party would want to have a committee chairman who doesn't know the first thing about what that committee is doing. The new committee chairman will almost certainly be the ranking member of the current committee.

The important thing to remember is that everyone knows what the next election can mean to the committee makeup. Therefore, the committee chairman is generally going to be courteous to the ranking member. After all, it won't take much to switch their positions, and what goes around comes around.

Specifically, if the committee chairman has called on one or two people to address the committee, he is almost certain to allow the ranking member to call at least one person to address the committee. You may well be that person.

Preparing for the hearing

HOWARD SHAFFER WAS A Congressional Fellow and served as a committee staff member in Washington. He is also a professional engineer, nuclear advocate, and has attended many hearings and testified before a committee of the Vermont legislature.

He emphasizes the importance of preparation. Visit the committee and the committee room before your presentation, if possible. Get a feeling for how the committee works and what the biases of the members might be. Look up the committee members on the web.

You address the chair as Mr. or Madame Chair. Be polite and deferential. Be there to help them have a successful meeting. Explain any technical terms you use: these people are probably on several committees, and they can't keep up with every term they hear. Allow plenty of time for questions.

Be early. Very early. Schedules change. If you are there early, you may well be called early.

Practice reading your testimony. It will be on the record as soon as you say it. The time for improvising is during the question period.

Thank the committee for inviting you when you are introduced. Thank them again at the end.

Your presentation to the committee

SINCE THIS IS A LEGISLATIVE COMMITTEE, even if the committee chairman has called someone else with very odd credentials to address the committee, you want to present your own credentials in a strong way. Perhaps take a short resume with you and give copies to the committee members. This is to show that you respect the committee, and the ranking member chose a good person to speak.

Robert Alvarez speaks to legislative committee in Montpelier, Vermont, April 18, 2013

On the other hand, don't feel you need to impress the committee. This advice, and much more, comes from Mike Hebert, Vermont state representative and ranking member of the House Committee on Energy. Hebert reminds us that committee members are regular people, just like you. Be yourself.

Be succinct. Keep to the relevant information. Ask how long a time you have for your testimony, and use less time than you are given. Give the important information first.

In terms of addressing the committee, you will be able to talk longer and be more technical than a letter to the editor or a public statement in the public-statement part of a hearing. But don't get carried away.

Written material should not be distributed until *after* you have spoken. Then you can distribute it. You want the committee members to be looking at you and interacting and asking questions, not heads down reading a handout.

Also, committee rooms are small, and it is always good to have one or two friends with you, but don't try to get a crowd to come. Though you can be more technical (supposedly, by being on this committee, the members have learned something about the issues), it is still best to speak simply, without jargon, and make your talk clear and approachable. Bring copies of your talk, also. Sometimes that is helpful.

For most of us advocates, we are happy if we can get one pro-nuclear person testifying in front of a committee. But in some cases, several people may testify on our side. It is important that the people who are testifying talk to each other ahead of time and are familiar with what the other people will say. Try not to contradict each other. The committee will be drawn to inconsistencies. If you are lucky enough to get several people before the committee, take the time to get your mutual act together.

If there is a TV camera at the hearing, make a point of looking at it when you come to a good sound bite in your talk. Actually, plan at least one good sound bite in your talk. This may be the only image seen on the evening news.

And here is an odd point, but a good one. The people holding the hearing, the people on the committee, may be bored out of their minds. They have to sit there and hear speaker after speaker. (A very accomplished person gave me this clue. I attend a committee so rarely that it seems like a Big Deal to me. It feels different for the people on the committee.) If there is a way you can say something like, "I understand some of the issues you face in considering this legislation, and these are my ideas for resolving these issues," *and* you look at the committee members . . . you might even get a dialog going. This is far better than you giving a canned speech while they try to look alert. As in many talks of many kinds, the question period is the important part.

Speaking and writing

IN THE CHAPTER ON SPEAKING at a hearing, I recommended bringing a handout with references. This is even more important when you speak to a legislative committee. In many cases, the committee record will include "supplemental material," and you should bring some well-referenced handouts. You can get data and references into the record this way.

The next step

SO, YOU HAVE SPOKEN TO the committee. Has it done any good? Frankly, not directly. Committee members are unlikely to change their opinion due to a presentation, though some may be interested enough to ask questions that show they have indeed understood something that is new to them.

To some extent, you are not there for the committee. You are there so that any report of the committee meeting, any video, anything, will mention that pro and con viewpoints were presented. Reporters may interview you. You may have a sound bite on TV or radio. This is all good.

Appearing before a committee is a lot of work, but being there breaks down the idea that everyone opposes nuclear energy.

And who knows? You may even influence a committee member. It has happened.

ACTION ITEM:

Food for thought. Someone in your group can speak to a committee. That's the point of this section. Still, this is pretty advanced activism. Not everyone will do this. For most people, just keep these ideas in mind when you read a newspaper report about something that happens in a legislative committee.

Note: I am not a lawyer, and the following is not legal advice. A citizen can speak to a legislative committee on occasion: that is the right of a citizen. However, if activism at the statehouse becomes an important part of your advocacy, you must look up the rules about registering as a lobbyist. You should consult a lawyer to get clarity on this issue.

CHAPTER THIRTY

THEIR BIG SPEAKER

NUCLEAR OPPONENTS EXIST WORLDWIDE, and they cooperate with each other. I am not sure how they arrange this, but every now and again the opponents will have a Big Speaker coming through your area on a world tour.

In my own area, we have had a physician from Germany who spoke on a study that supposedly showed that children who live near nuclear plants get leukemia. Helen Caldicott has come through town, and she spoke to the energy committee of our legislature. A woman who wrote a terrifying book about the consequences of Fukushima also visited. There was a book about Chernobyl, *Voices from Chernobyl* by Svetlana Alexievich, who won a Nobel Prize for her work. The book was more of an indictment of the Soviet system than of nuclear power, in my opinion. It was one of several books by that author about Soviet mismanagement: for example, *Zinky Boys: Soviet Voices from the Afghanistan War*. However, the Chernobyl book was also an indictment of nuclear power. A local woman turned the Chernobyl book into a short play, and the play toured the Northeast. The play was read aloud at various meetings. It was heavily (if misleadingly) advertised, as I described in a blog post at the time.

So, if you live near a nuclear plant, you can expect some of the Big Guns to show up near you. Is there something you can or should do about this?

Well, yes there is. You should remember that going to these meetings can be quite stressful, and that activism is a smorgasbord of activities. You should go hear their Big Speaker if that works for you.

I have never been able to say, Yes, activists should always do *that*. Whatever *that* might be, the activist's effectiveness in doing *that* will depend on the activist, and the match between the activist and the activity. As Howard Shaffer says, "There is no silver bullet to activism; there's only silver buckshot."

Go see their Big Speaker if that works for you.

Why to go to their Big Speaker

THERE ARE THREE main reasons to go to the Big Speaker.

1. To find out what they say and how people react

In other words, gathering information about opposition strategies.

This can be important, or it can be useless. Sometimes, the opposition speaker will reveal their new strategies and their planned next steps. This can be useful to know about. However, in many cases, it won't be useful. The opposition speakers tend to be very repetitive. (Sometimes I think I could give their talks myself, I have heard the arguments so often.) Also, their Big Speaker probably has a book out, or gave interviews that are now available on YouTube, or the paper in the next town over— where they stopped before they came to your town—reviewed their talk. So you can find out most of the information without leaving the comfort of your home.

In other words, I am not much for attending unpleasant meetings in order to gather intelligence. But I also hate going to such meetings. Other activists, who go to many of these meetings, get more out of their attendance at the meetings. They pick up nuances in the opponents' plans. I would probably never have noticed.

2. To get opposing views in the press

To be noticed by the press, you should plan to ask at least one question that shows your beliefs are opposite to those of the speaker. When you ask this question, be sure to identify yourself by name and possibly by background: "I am Meredith Angwin and I blog at *Yes Vermont Yankee*." Introduce yourself quite briefly, but you want the reporters to notice you.

When you are there, you should combat (very politely) misinformation. Be there when the reporters are there. Always be polite: you are *not* there to disrupt the meeting. But you can ask questions and make statements that combat misinformation. When you do your homework before the meeting, find out what the speaker usually says. Pick one of two of the more outrageous statements and bring a reference that rebuts it. Mention the reference if you can. This has nothing to do with whether the *person* will take you seriously . . . the goal is for the reporters to take you seriously. Ask those polite questions.

Reporters want a "he said, she said" story, so they may want to quote you. They may be very willing to talk to you. Buttonhole reporters afterward and explain that you just want to clarify what you said in the meeting. You want to give them a better reference. You are there to help them get both sides of the story. Practice an elevator speech, and give it.

Be both polite and noticeable. It isn't easy in a room full of people who totally disagree with you. But it can be worth doing.

When you change the press coverage, you move the needle of opinion.

3. With concentrated effort, you can sometimes change how the speaker behaves

This is truly advanced activism and not for the faint of heart. It is important to be polite, or it could be considered harassment.

Ask the same questions in several venues. Come up with a great set of questions. The speaker will be making a tour, probably speaking in several nearby towns. Go to each place and ask the same questions. Remember to be polite, even gentle in your tone. You are just trying to get your point across in several venues. You cannot come across as strident or harassing. In one case where some friends of mine did this, in the third town, the speaker stopped taking questions from the audience. Well, enough about that. This is tough to do, and very tough to do well.

The falsehood express

JUST FOR FUN: A BRIEF COMPENDIUM of some types of falsehoods by the opponents. Know the falsehoods and be ready to debunk them in public.

- Outright lies. For example, a claim that the fuel pool at Fukushima 4 burned and spread radiation. The New York Times reported successful removal of fuel from the fuel pool.[110]

- Misleading graphics. The chart of "Fukushima contamination spreading across the Pacific" is actually a chart of wave heights from the tsunami. The NOAA attribution and measurements in centimeters is a bit of a giveaway. This chart is even debunked in Snopes.[111] But you can still see the chart being presented as Fukushima radiation.

- False sampling. This is a more sophisticated one. Let's say that there is a population of 10,000 women, and 10 percent of them are redheads. If you take repeated random samples of 100, you will eventually find a sample that is 90 percent redheads. Then you can use this sample to prove that redheads are taking over the world! This kind of cherry picking is common among the anti-nuclear crowd. For example, very little radiation made it across the Pacific from Fukushima. The radiation was far too small to do any harm or cause any deaths. Of course, there was no change in infant mortality on the West Coast due to radiation.

However, by checking statistics for town after town, one nuclear opponent found widely separated towns that had increases in infant mortality after Fukushima. (Of course, there were many other towns showing decreased mortality or no change.) Just like "the redheads are taking over the world," this researcher claimed these towns proved that Fukushima was killing American babies.[112] This technique is used surprisingly often. You have to be ready to move their arguments to fuller samples and point out the errors.

- False advertising. Several anti-nuclear groups had arranged for a meeting room at the local Montshire Museum of Science to present the play, *Voices of Chernobyl*. In their advertising, they made it look as if the Montshire (a very loved and respected institution) was sponsoring the play. When I called the number on the ad, they would not tell me who was sponsoring it.[113]

- The usual fear mongering with sound bites. "Around nuclear plants, we really pay our utility bills at the hospital." "There is no safe level of radiation." "Consider the children!"

This is only a brief survey, but I suspect most people won't want to go to their Big Speaker. So I am giving only the 30,000-foot view of attending.

Going to see their Big Speaker is an advanced taste (or whatever you want to call it). But if you do it, enjoy it, ask questions, and you will move the needle of public opinion.

ACTION ITEM:

Watch their Big Speaker. Watch a video on YouTube of a nuclear opponent speaking. Decide if it would be helpful for you to attend such a meeting in person.

CHAPTER THIRTY-ONE

READY FOR THEIR RALLY

NUCLEAR OPPONENTS hold many rallies. Some are big (hundreds of people marched through Brattleboro) and some are relatively small. Every occasion seems to call for at least a "vigil" with a few people dressed in black and looking sad about the deaths and dangers of nuclear energy. Frankly, it would drive a person crazy to try to attend all of these.

Once again, we have the smorgasbord concept. You can go to their rally, and in many cases this will be worthwhile. But only if it is your cuppa, so to speak.

This chapter will be about

- Why attend an opponent rally,
- Choosing which rally to attend, and
- What to do at an opponent rally.

Why attend an opponent rally

YOU ATTEND AN OPPONENT rally to get publicity for your cause, and to break the "everyone hates nuclear" publicity they are attempting to gather for their own cause.

Also, at smaller rallies, you can talk to opponents sometimes. The opponents who are not leaders of the rally may well want to talk with you.

The leaders are set in their ways, and you are merely an annoyance to them. (Which you are, at some level, trying to be. You are trying to break the steadily one-sided publicity they are trying to encourage.) But many people just turned out for the rally because it seemed a good thing to do, or because their friends were going, or because it was announced at the Sierra Club meeting about black bear habitat. These people are anti-nuclear also, but they are sometimes intrigued by the idea that someone, standing right in front of them, is pro-nuclear. How can that be? What kind of evil person would do that? But you don't look like an evil person. They may want to talk to you.

You may be able to move the needle of their thoughts, just a little. Don't expect "road to Damascus" conversion experiences, but you may have some effect on their thinking. Any mitigation in their views toward nuclear is a win for you.

Once again (gosh, it does get repetitive), if you are at an opponent rally, you are there to obtain publicity. You must be visible. You must be willing to talk to reporters afterwards.

It is good if you can speak to some of the opponents, but sometimes they will not speak with you, and sometimes you wish they hadn't spoken to you when they do speak. At a rally, one opponent leader told me to "Have a nice cancer." (I thought, "Same to you, buddy," but I didn't say it.)

So, the main thing . . . being visible.

You are there to be visible, but you are not there to be confrontational. It's not about the opponents: if they harass you, de-escalate. Don't get angry and don't begin harassing them. Remember . . . it's not about the opponents. It's about the cameras.

Basically, aim to get in the media photos (still and video), and take your own pictures. Yes, take pictures of yourself being at the rally.

You can put the pictures on your blog, put them on Facebook, tweet them, etc. Also, keep your eye on the reporters and TV cameramen. Try to get interviews with reporters and try to get in front of the cameras.

Don't worry too much about being pushy . . . if you don't literally *push* somebody, you aren't being pushy, in my opinion. I still remember a time when a reporter was interviewing Howard Shaffer. An opponent, complete with carried sign, literally pushed her way between the two of them. You won't do that, of course. But think about what she did, and don't be shy about getting your sign in front of the camera.

By being at the rally, and even getting a little bit of publicity, you will move the needle from the perception that "everybody hates nuclear." You do the reporters a favor: they want "he said, she said," but the plant probably won't comment. You are there, and that gives them the "he said" that they want.

Choosing a rally

IN GENERAL, opponent rallies can be divided into two types:
- Issue-based rallies
- "Memorial" rallies

Nuclear supporters and opponents rally in front of Brattleboro courthouse, September 12, 2011, at beginning of hearing about Vermont Yankee.

An issue-based rally is about an issue. For example, at Vermont Yankee, there were several court hearings, and opponents often rallied in front of the courthouse. Or perhaps a small amount of tritium escapes from the plant . . . too little to be detected anywhere except a test well, but an opportunity for opponents to show up at the plant gates. That's an issue rally.

A memorial rally is about a "big date." Around here, opponents hold memorial rallies about Hiroshima (which was part of a war, not part of the electricity grid), Chernobyl, Three Mile Island, and Fukushima. The good news is that you know the rally is coming. The bad news is that, in my opinion, it is not worth going to them. Except for Hiroshima (there was a war on, as you recall), radiation casualties were nonexistent in some cases (Three Mile Island, Fukushima) or small compared to other industrial accidents (Chernobyl). But this is a hard case to make with a few posters on a public street. It would be easy to look hardhearted (just a *few* deaths) or even look just plain weird.

And it is useless to try to talk about these past problems while standing on the street. You can't change the past. Fighting one view of history with an alternate view is best left to historians, opinion pieces in newspapers, magazine articles, books, and scholarly articles in scholarly journals. History is history. While re-interpreting history can change over time (most Americans have a different view of Manifest Destiny than I was taught as a child), it is not a subject that lends itself to sound bites.

In other words, if you are going to go to an opponent rally, go to an issue rally.

Issue rallies: the alternative story

AT AN ISSUE RALLY, you can tell a story with a more positive view than the opponents will present. Nuclear supporters can tell an upbeat story about the future. You can show that this issue can be resolved in a way that is to everyone's advantage.

Before meeting the press, think about how to express your positive emotions toward nuclear. Bring your emotions and your facts to the signs and the reporters.

After all, as an activist, you are working to change the future. Don't get caught up rehashing the past.

What to do at an opponent rally

RALLIES ARE EXCITING, and emotions can run high. Keep your cool! Sometimes this is pretty hard to do. You don't need to respond to every negative comment. If you feel like you're being attacked, ignore it, turn away, or walk away. Don't trade insults. Take the high road.

Don't be a doormat, but aim to de-escalate any negative situation. There will always be people watching and cameras rolling. You don't want the evening news to show a clip of you shouting angrily at an opponent. Anyway, back to the rally itself.

Once again, the point is to get some publicity. At a good rally, you can also build solidarity and fellow feeling among your supporters. Being at a rally together is a tremendously bonding experience. That is one of the reasons the opponents do it so often. So, let's talk about three aspects of being at opponent rallies.

- Bonding and friendship
- Increasing the commitment of your supporters
- Publicity

Bonding and friendship

ALWAYS GO TO AN OPPONENT rally with someone else. Be with friends. (Or at least one friend. Howard Shaffer and I have gone to rallies at the last minute, just the two of us.) Be visible. At rallies, you can wear distinctive clothing as you can at hearings. Unlike hearings, however, your visuals are basically all-important. Standing together in similar clothes, you feel like a team.

Increasing the commitment of your supporters

IT IS BEST IF YOU CAN HAVE some kind of food event after the rally at a restaurant or at someone's home. One time when we were out there at the same time as the opponents, one member of our group persuaded a local business to open the employee break room for us, and another member of our group showed up with treats from a donut shop. This does not have to be fancy, but there's a kind of secret to this: if you have put yourself out to be on the street, with opponents also out there, and then you get together, the camaraderie is quite amazing. These become the *we few, we happy few, we band of brothers.*

We are the supporters. Everyone loved the after-rally meeting. It was a spectacular event. "It was the best part," as one man said. There's a chance to talk and to get to know other people who share many of your values, at least in terms of energy.

Weirdly, opponent rallies can also be a fundraising opportunity for your group. For example, for one rally, I had ordered t-shirts, which I gave away freely so that we would all be recognizable as nuclear supporters. People asked how much the t-shirts cost. Well, the things were special order and they cost about $20. (I wish I had ordered more. People loved them and ordering more would have brought the price down.) People asked to pay for their shirts. I was ashamed to tell them this high price. But nobody thought it was high. Instead, people were thrusting $20, $30, $50 at me to pay for the t-shirts. If I was a clever fundraiser, I could have done something with this phenomenon.

Publicity

AT A HEARING, IT'S MOSTLY about what you say. At a rally, it's mostly about the visuals.

I think I have spoken enough about t-shirts for now. Dressing for visibility is important. However, at a rally, you also have another way to be visible: signs. Carry some signs! They are easy to make and, frankly, the homemade ones are more authentic-looking anyway. We got some signs from PopAtomic Studios.[114] We also obtained a few VY4VT signs from the power plant (which had made many such signs for people to put on their lawns, and were happy to give us a few to hold or put on sticks). Most of our signs were handmade.

When you make your own sign, think visibility. Color contrast, strong colors, and big letters. This is not a disquisition on the virtues of nuclear power: this is a simple statement. Nuclear: Electricity without the Carbon! Nuclear: Safe and Clean for Vermont! That sort of thing. Depending on the rally, a pickup truck can be very helpful. At one of our rallies, the union people sent a pickup truck, which parked right outside the zone where the police had declared "no parking." We were able to stand on top of the pickup with our signs . . . now, *that* is visibility.

There are pictures of the rally at my blog[115] and at the American Nuclear Society blog[116].

This side of the law

OH. THE POLICE. OBEY THEM, of course. If they don't want you to step off the sidewalk, don't step off the sidewalk. It is tempting to do so, because your opponents will target your signs with bigger signs of their own and you want to get in front of them. But don't. (I did once, and had the embarrassment of having a police officer ask me to step back. Not my finest activist moment.)

In general, you need to inform police about rallies. However, if you are just showing up at an opponent rally, you can assume that either the opponents have informed the police or, if they haven't, they will be the ones in trouble. In general, there will be fewer of you than the opponents. They have been organizing for rallies for a long time, and they have it down about getting a crowd. So—you don't have to worry much about informing people.

While people have, constitutionally, the right to freely assemble, a rally could require a permit, just as a parade might require a permit. The best way to deal with this is to assess the situation quietly: ask someone knowledgeable about the rules. The problem is that once you show up at city hall with a question, the people in the office *have* to pull out all the stops (parade permit, questions about who pays for extra police if necessary, etc.), when actually they would much rather ignore the situation since they already have their hands full with the opponents. This is one of the reasons that joining an opponent rally can be easier than planning your own.

When you plan your own rally, of course, you need to be more proactive in making sure it is okay with the town authorities.

Speaking of the sidewalk. Nobody owns it, and if you are too spread out, opponents will walk between the people in your group, and those opponents will be holding the biggest signs possible. They do this to diminish the visual impact of your group. Stick relatively close together. The opponents don't want to touch or shove you, just as you don't want to touch or shove them. It's a dance out there, with no perfect moves. Just do your best. I don't recommend pushing into opponent groups, because I think the effect of a mass of pro-nuclear people is more eye-catching and camera-catching.

Be ready to give interviews, during or after the rally. I introduced myself to a cameraman during a rally. Then I was sure he was ignoring me. But as the rally broke up, he asked me to come over so he could ask a few questions. So my self-introduction worked. You never know what will work.

When asked a question, try for succinct answers: you may get, quite literally, less than ten seconds of airtime. The good news is that you *are* getting airtime, and the story will be "both sides rallied today" instead of "everyone hates nuclear." Opposing viewpoints make good stories. Often reporters will want you to say a few words—not because they love nuclear, but because they want to write or videotape an interesting story.

I was just thinking about the fact that our t-shirts were white, and the opponents were "vigiling," as usual, in black. It kind of reminds me of Bogart's line in to Ingrid Bergman in *Casablanca:* "The Germans wore gray, and you wore blue."

Be visible. And wear the white hats, not the black.

We will always have Paris

ANOTHER LINE FROM CASABLANCA is also relevant. You can get publicity, you can move the needle, and your facility can still be forced to close. You can do your best, but you cannot control the outcome.

However, with rallies, especially the slightly scary ones where you and the opponents are both out there (yes, I am a coward), you can have so much camaraderie and such good memories that the other Bogart line from *Casablanca*, comes into play. When Rick and Ingrid separate forever, near the end of the movie, Rick says:

"*We will always have Paris.*"

They will always remember their time together in Paris.

And you and your friends will always remember that rally. You will always have . . . whatever city the rally was in. In my case, I will always have Brattleboro.

ACTION ITEM:

Signs. What signs would you like to carry at a rally? Can you make those signs right now? (Be Prepared.)

CHAPTER THIRTY-TWO

READY FOR YOUR RALLY

ONCE AGAIN, REMEMBER that pro-nuclear activism is a smorgasbord of activities, not a forced march to some impossible goal. Most pro-nuclear advocates never hold a rally. You could argue that any time spent planning a rally is time you could have spent speaking to a local group.

Yet, just like appearing at the opponent rally, holding a pro-nuclear rally can build friendship and camaraderie, and show the world (through media coverage of the rally) that nuclear power is supported by ordinary people. It's not just anti-nuclear people who get out there and talk to the press; it's you, too.

Many aspects of holding a pro-nuclear rally are the same as how to appear and act at opponent rallies. I will not repeat these here. T-shirts, colorful signs, talking to reporters, and having an after-rally meal or snack are just as important for your own rallies as for appearing at anti-nuclear rallies. In this chapter, I will cover issues unique to hosting your own rally.

Planning your rally

THESE ISSUES ARE MOSTLY about planning. For the opponent rally, you basically just show up . . . they take care of the rest for you. For your own rally, you will have to decide:

- When to hold it
- Where to hold it
- What permissions you may need (parade permits, private property issues)
- How to tell your supporters you are having a rally
- Notifying the press and making sure it is covered in the press

Let's get started on your very own pro-nuclear rally!

When to hold it

MANY FACTORS GO INTO this decision. For example, I am fond of holding rallies on St. Patrick's Day. In most places, the worst of the winter weather is over, and in other places, the worst of the summer heat is yet to come. I have held a successful rally on this day, and so has a group in California: Californians for Green Nuclear Power.

That's another thing about St. Patrick's Day. It is associated with the color green, and that can translate quickly into *green* nuclear power. It also gives some guidance on how to dress, and what color to make the signs.

Also, it is a few days after the anniversary of the great Eastern Japan Earthquake. Most people forget the earthquake and remember the meltdown of the Fukushima plant instead. Opponents often hold vigils and so forth on March 11. In

Californians for Green Nuclear Power rally, St. Patrick's Day, 2016, San Luis Obispo. Heather Matteson holding sign.   Credit: Gene Nelson, Ph.D.

some ways, your rally of March 17 capitalizes on the publicity they generate.

At your rally, you need to be ready to answer questions about Fukushima, of course. A surprising number of people don't know that nobody died or was badly injured by radiation. People drowned, cranes fell and crushed people, trains were washed away. Radiation only caused very minor injuries to three power plant workers. Even if you can only get *that* across, it will be a benefit.

Of course, you don't want to limit yourself to St. Patrick's Day. This is not the only day that can work. You can celebrate your own anniversaries. Not vigils—hold a celebratory rally. The anniversary of the day the local plant came online. The anniversary of the day the first commercial reactor came online. There are many things to celebrate.

One of our best rallies was when Entergy decided to refuel Vermont Yankee, despite ongoing court cases that looked as if Entergy might have to shut the plant down. We held a rally on the plant grounds during the refueling outage. During shift change, we held signs welcoming the shift workers and congratulating everyone on the continued run of Vermont Yankee. The plant had just finished an excellent breaker-to-breaker run, and we celebrated that also. We waved at the workers coming in for their shifts. Most of the time, if the workers see someone with a sign, that person is against the plant. We had signs, but we were in favor of plant operation. The people who worked at the plant were very appreciative of our support.

And so, without much ado, we move to the next question.

Where to hold it

BASICALLY, THERE ARE TWO CHOICES: private property and public property.

If you hold a rally on public property, if it is a small rally that won't block traffic, in many cases, you can just hold it. You will get publicity, and you will be surprised at how many people will honk and wave and support you (or walk by and say something supportive). On the other hand, for bigger rallies, you probably have to check with police first and may need to get some kind of permit.

Another thing about public property is that it is public. I have never heard of anything bad happening at a pro-nuclear rally, but judge your own situation. If you think you will need paid security guards, you should reconsider where you hold the rally.

St Patrick's Day Rally at Vermont Yankee, near the plant gates, 2012.
William Schulze, Twarog family, myself in background.

For private property, the obvious place is the nuclear facility you are supporting. Most such places have an area that is their property, but not within a strong security perimeter. For example, a long driveway, or an office building used for press conferences or whatever, on the way into the plant. Or it could be on plant property but on the outside of the barbed wire. This can be an excellent place to hold the rally, assuming you get permission from the plant. You can get newspapers and reporters to come, as long as the plant is okay with it. Sometimes the plant will allow you to hold your after-rally meeting in their outside-the-inner-fence building. They may even provide pizza.

As you can see, the date and reasons for the rally, and the place of the rally, are not totally independent variables.

Permissions and private property issues

IF YOU ARE ON PLANT PROPERTY, you just have to obey their rules. Park where they ask you to park, arrive and leave when they ask you to leave. Take pictures of the people at the rally, but don't take pictures of the fence or the security cameras or anything else of that kind. It's not actually too restrictive.

If you are holding a rally in a park or on a street, if it is at all big, make sure you have let the local police know about it and gotten any permissions you need from the town.

Maybe I shouldn't say this, but we all know that some things fly under the radar. If you have less than fifteen people and you will be there less than an hour, you may not need to do this. Talk to someone who knows. But remember, it's not like the opponent rallies, where they do the permission work for you.

How to tell your supporters you are holding this rally

TELL THEM EVERY WAY YOU CAN. Tell them on Facebook, send out an announcement to the email list, send another announcement to the email list two days later, tweet it, and so forth. Announce it at local ANS meetings, put it on your blog. In short, publicize it!

Frankly, the two things that are key are word of mouth and your email list. Third is your blog. Those are the ways that will get supporters to show up. By the way, by "word of mouth" I also recommend contacting the unions that work at the plant. The leaders should also be on your email lists, of course. You never know . . . a bunch of people may come . . . possibly with a pickup truck.

Notifying the press

FIND YOUR EMAIL LIST AND SEND an email announcing the rally well in advance. Think about what media outlets have covered your activities in the past. If you have been on a friendly talk show, call the host and ask if you can visit his show to talk about the purpose of your rally. Your aim is to get reporters to cover your rally.

Hopefully, you will get some reporters from local papers, and farther-away papers will pick up their posts.

Whether this happens or not, after the rally, put lots of your own pics of the rally on Facebook, on your blog, on all the social media. Make it clear that a lot of people were there and a good time was had by all.

It is great if mainstream media documents your rally, but remember that documenting it yourself is very worthwhile. People who were there will like to see their pictures on your blog. Reporters who ask about it later can be referred to your blog. You may be able to write guest posts about it for other pro-nuclear blogs. Your rally was an important event, and you should shout about it.

Did it matter?

DID IT MATTER? That is always a big question, no matter what you do. And the answer is always, yes. You may or may not succeed at your immediate goal. However, when the public sees a group of people supporting nuclear power in public—this is something that always matters in the long run.

ACTION ITEM:

Think of your rally. Play with the idea of holding a pro-nuclear St. Patrick's Day rally. Who would you invite? Where would you hold it?

CHAPTER THIRTY-THREE

NOT THE FINALE

I WANT TO WRITE a chapter about how everything turns out well, now that people such as Mary and Jennifer are defending the plant and Joe's publicity is more upbeat and . . .

Life, however, is not that simple. There's rarely a triumphant moment, with swelling strings and sunrises and so forth. Life is not a movie. And nobody can personally "save" a nuclear facility.

And yet, people can move the needle toward a wider favorable opinion of nuclear energy. Things can, indeed, improve, both for the plant and its supporters.

First steps

JENNIFER SEES MARY'S LETTER in the paper and calls her. They meet for coffee and talk a little about their lives and their husbands. They also talk about other women they know who might be pro-nuclear. Jennifer thinks that maybe a coffee meeting at her house would be a good place to invite the women and so forth. Awkwardly, Mary says that, for a first meeting, some of the wives might find Jennifer's sumptuous home off-putting. Mary thinks the first meeting should be at her home. Jennifer is slightly miffed, but agrees. The first meeting is at Mary's house, the second at Jennifer's house. At the first meeting, we will write letters, Jennifer suggests. Mary agrees.

But they have got to reach out to somebody more than the wives. But who? Jennifer gets very brave and suggests that the two of them give a talk at her alumni association meeting. Jennifer is thinking that the women who walked off after the yoga class . . . were they just avoiding conflict, or did some of them actually agree with her?

After a few moments' discussion, though, Mary and Jennifer decide they aren't ready for this yet. Mary suggests that maybe one of the plant outreach people can talk to the alumni group. Seems like a good idea, but neither woman is sure how to act on it. Mary says she will look into it: maybe she can find someone at the plant who will give a talk at the alumni meeting.

Jennifer says that there are committee meetings about the plant, just all the time, at the state capital. Water permits, petitions to shut the plant down being considered by committees, all sorts of stuff. She suggests that they can plan to attend one of the meetings, maybe carpool. Mary is a little worried they are getting ahead of themselves, but why not? The state capital is less than 100 miles away, and it could be a very informative outing. They decide to go. At the least, this will give them more information for letters to the editor.

Meanwhile, Joseph the plant manager continues to have more good feelings. The usual puppets showed up for the

Fukushima commemoration, but there were quite a few letters (well, four letters) in the local paper that explained that radiation from Fukushima was not a problem for the United States and only a problem in a comparatively small part of the actual prefecture in Japan. Two were from the women who had written letters before, but two more letters seem to have been inspired by the first two letters. There was a letter from a man who is a retired electrical engineer and one from a high school student who had read a book called *Power to Save the World*. Interesting. Maybe he should read that book.

Meanwhile, perhaps he could encourage some of his people to reach out to younger people. The plant is one of the best sources of jobs in the area, but he wasn't sure if the plant had ever showed up at the high school Career Day. He'd ask Ellen Beaty, the press and outreach coordinator.

They could go to Career Days at the local high school and junior colleges. That might be a good start. And who was that guy from South Carolina who called him? Apparently, in South Carolina, there were teacher-training workshops about nuclear energy, and this man was suggesting he could share the training materials. Joseph wasn't sure his own management would agree to something so visible and radical, but he would at least ask to see the teacher-training material.

Also, he has the Women in Nuclear group at the plant. He knows that, but day-to-day business has always gotten in the way of doing anything official with them, beyond giving them some meeting space. Perhaps they could be involved in some kind of outreach. They could be very effective, he thinks.

The needle moves . . .

ONE PERSON CAN MAKE A DIFFERENCE. A couple of people can make a big difference. The sight of one person being pro-nuclear can encourage others.

It takes courage to take the first step, and results may not seem very dramatic. But just as people got used to the idea that women should vote (because women kept saying so) and that gay people should have the right to marry (because gay people kept saying so), the first step in changing society is that the people must step *out* of their cloistered little worlds and make their arguments to larger groups in society.

Once a person has stepped out of the quiet little cloister, there will be unexpected support, as well as the expected scorn.

There's a smorgasbord of actions you can take. Start taking some of them.

When you close this book, go to your computer and write a pro-nuclear letter to the editor. Campaign for clean air and reliable power. Campaign for clean, safe, and abundant energy.

And be proud of yourself for helping to make this a better world for our children and grandchildren.

ACKNOWLEDGEMENTS

SO MANY PEOPLE HELPED ME and supported me in bringing this book to completion! In many ways, I hardly know where to start with acknowledgements. But I have to start somewhere.

First and foremost, my husband Dr. George Angwin, who supported me wholeheartedly on this project. He made it clear that he believed this book was important. George was the main editor and publisher of our previous book, *Voices for Vermont Yankee*. That book is a compendium of statements in favor of Vermont Yankee: the statements were originally made to the Vermont Public Service Board. I also thank my daughter Julia Angwin, son-in-law Vijay Modi, and my son and daughter-in-law Ilan and Mari Pazhoor Angwin for inspiring and nurturing me throughout this process. I also thank my granddaughter Mira for making "book" stickers to put in my planning calendar in order to block out time for the book. Such stickers are not usually available! They are special stickers, made just for me.

Next, I need to thank Lindsay Rose. Without her, this book would have taken much longer and been much worse. Before working with me on this book, Rose was at Vermont Yankee, and then spokesperson for Palisades. She was my "assistant" on this book, if "assistant" covers researcher, organizer, fact-checker, contributor and cheerleader. I am especially indebted to her for her insight on the dreaded "elevator speech." Rose was a tremendous asset to the project, and I was very lucky to be able to work with her.

After that, I thank Howard Shaffer, who introduced me to pro-nuclear advocacy and has always been my guide. Rod Adams, blogger extraordinaire, has been a model, a mentor, and a friend, for years. There are some people who it would take many pages to thank properly. Thanking Howard and Rod would be like writing a memoir.

With sorrow, I note that Brian Cosgrove passed away while I was finalizing this book. Cosgrove was a great friend and tireless fighter for Vermont Yankee. His memory is a blessing in my life.

I have been fortunate to make many friends in my life as a nuclear advocate. Many of them reviewed earlier drafts of the book and shared their expert opinions. I thank Guy Page, a former newspaper owner and currently communication director of the Vermont Energy Partnership. Page was very generous in sharing his expertise in working effectively with newspapers and other media. Thanks to Eugene S. Grecheck, past president of the American Nuclear Society, for sharing his experience speaking to public groups; Mike Hebert, state representative and ranking member of the House Committee on Natural Resources and Energy, Vermont, for his valuable insight on preparing to speak in front of a legislative committee; Patty O'Donnell, business owner and former state representative for Vernon, Vermont, for sharing her experiences facilitating speaking engagements for Vermont Yankee employees; Laura Scheele of Idaho National Laboratory Public Affairs group reviewed parts of the book, and her review inspired the action items at the end of each chapter; Edward Kee of Nuclear Economics Consulting Group and Fritz Schneider of Clark Communications for their advice on talking to and building relationships with the media; Tamar Cerafici, environmental lawyer specializing in nuclear regulation, who suggested that we needed to include a section on press releases and elevator speeches; Dr. Ann Bisconti of Bisconti Research for sharing her research results; Marie-Christine Hupé for sharing her inspiring story; Jaro Franto for introducing me to Mlle. Hupé; Dr. Gene Nelson for sharing his photograph of the St. Patrick's Day rally in support of Diablo Canyon; Steve Aplin for permission to use the carbon counter on his blog as an example of blogging (and for everything else he does); Gwyneth Cravens for inspiring me through her book *Power to Save the World* and for coming to Vermont and for everything she does; and to Sheldon, Tara, and Reagan Shippee—the challenges they faced as a "nuclear" family was the inspiration for some of the events in the lives of the book's fictional characters.

I thank many people who are active or officers in the American Nuclear Society (ANS): Will Davis, Margaret Harding, Gail Marcus, and Eric Loewen especially. And thanks to American Nuclear Society staff, past and present, and especially to Rick Michal, Tracy Coyle and Linda Zec. I am constantly appreciative of everything the ANS does, both at national and local levels. I thank Andrew Dawson, David

Hess, and Caroline Peachey for encouragement and helpful conversations. It's good to have friends on both sides of the pond! I also thank Peachey for the opportunity to write articles for *Nuclear Engineering International* magazine.[117]

And then there are the people who reviewed the book quite carefully, but did not want to share their names. I thank them. When you work for a big business, sometimes you can't share your name without seeming to be a "spokesperson." I know who these people are (because I sent chapters of the book to them), and I thank them!

I thank the people in California for the inspiration they give to everyone through starting so many groups and pursuing so many paths to advocacy. I cannot name them all, but I want to give a special shout-out to Michael Shellenberger, Dr. Bob Greene, Dr. Gene Nelson, William Gloege, Ted Nordhaus, Dr. Alex Cannara, Heather Matteson, and Kristin Zaitz.

Many others have been constant supporters in my life as a nuclear advocate, a scholar, and an educator. I thank Christy Tryhus of Mission Marketing Mentors for her guidance on the book project, and Greg London for his supportive guidance on all my projects over the years; Ronda Rawlins and Michelle DeFilippo of 1106 Design for pulling the final book together; the Twarog family for their steady and unwavering support of Vermont Yankee; Dan Yurman for support in general; John McClaughry, founder of the Ethan Allen Institute and his wife Anne for their kindness and support; Dr. Robert Hargraves for inspiration and sharing his expertise; Suzy Hobbs Baker, founder of PopAtomic Studios for creating beautiful rally signs that pro-nuclear supporters carried throughout Vermont; Les

Corrice for his careful reporting on Fukushima; and John Dobken of Energy Northwest for great conversations and the opportunity to publish on the Northwest Clean Energy Blog. I thank Mimi Holland Limbach of Potomac Communications Group for her effective nuclear advocacy and for reminding me that reporters go home before the meeting ends. I thank Richard Schmidt for his above-and-beyond help and support for Vermont Yankee, including the day when the two of us faced two nuclear opponents in an early morning radio broadcast debate.

I thank Areva for a wonderful and informative tour of their enrichment and reprocessing facilities in France. Several pro-nuclear advocates took the tour in 2010. Thank you to all my tour companions, to Areva, and to Jarret Adams, who led the tour. (Jarret is now CEO at Full On Communications in Washington, D.C.) I am grateful for the assistance of those who have provided reviews, comments, and ideas for this book.

I also want to admit, wholeheartedly, that this book is not the complete story. There are advocates who have supported nuclear energy in important and innovative ways—advocates and activities not even mentioned in this book. I am truly sorry. It is impossible to tell the complete story on nuclear advocacy. I apologize to all the people I have left out of the book because of my ignorance of their activities, the book's space constraints, or time (to do research).

I thank all the people who supported Vermont Yankee and made efforts to keep it running. So many people came to rallies, to hearings, wrote letters to the editor, wrote op-eds. So many people were advocates for the plant. They are all my friends, whether or not I have met them. Without them, it would not have occurred to me that I should write a book like this.

I have had a lot of encouragement, advice, and help while writing this book. However, any mistakes or errors are fully my own.

ENDNOTES

[1] George Angwin and Meredith Angwin, *Voices of Vermont Yankee* (Carnot Communications, 2013), https://www.amazon.com/Voices-Vermont-Yankee-George-Angwin-ebook/dp/B00BJ7KSTQ

[2] Gwyneth Cravens, *Power to Save the World* (Vintage: 2008). http://www.amazon.com/Power-Save-World-Nuclear-Energy/dp/0307385876

[3] William Tucker, *Terrestrial Energy: How Nuclear Energy Will Lead the Green Revolution and End America's Energy Odyssey* (Bartleby, 2008). http://www.amazon.com/Terrestrial-Energy-Nuclear-Revolution-Americas/dp/0910155763

[4] Geoff Russell, *GreenJacked!: The Derailing of Environmental Action on Climate Change* (Amazon Digital Services, LLC: 2014). Kindle edition. https://www.amazon.com/GreenJacked-derailing-environmental-action-climate-ebook/dp/B00MN7UPH6?ie=UTF8&keywords=greenjacked&qid=1464615061&ref_=sr_1_1&s=books&sr=1-1

[5] http://www.ans.org/pi/news/article-213/

[6] http://www.nuclearmatters.com

[7] http://thebreakthrough.org/about/history/

[8] http://www.cgnp.org

[9] http://www.thoriumenergyalliance.com

[10] http://www.environmentalprogress.org

[11] http://mothersfornuclear.org

[12] http://www.nei.org/Knowledge-Center/Nuclear-Statistics/Environment-Emissions-Prevented/Emissions-Avoided-by-the-US-Nuclear-Industry

[13] Ashutosh Jogalekar, "Nuclear Power May Have Saved 1.8 Million Lives Otherwise Lost to Fossil Fuels, May Save Up to 7 Million More," *Scientific American*, April 2nd, 2013. Blog post. http://blogs.scientificamerican.com/

the-curious-wavefunction/nuclear-power-may-have-saved-1-8-million-lives-otherwise-lost-to-fossil-fuels-may-save-up-to-7-million-more/

[14] https://www3.epa.gov/pmdesignations/faq.htm

[15] http://www.southeastcoalash.org/?page_id=78

[16] https://www3.epa.gov/epawaste/nonhaz/industrial/special/fossil/ccrs-fs/

[17] http://www.utilitydive.com/news/two-years-after-epas-coal-ash-rule-progress-depends-on-states/419672/

[18] https://en.wikipedia.org/wiki/Life-cycle_greenhouse-gas_emissions_of_energy_sources.

[19] Institute for Energy Research, "New England Using More Natural Gas Following Vermont Yankee Closure," January 20th, 2016, http://institute forenergyresearch.org/analysis/new-england-using-more-natural-gas-following-vermont-yankee-closure/; Nuclear Energy Institute, "Fact Sheet," http://www.nei.org/Master-Document-Folder/Backgrounders/Fact-Sheets/Nuclear-Energy-America-s-Low-Carbon-Electricity-Le

[20] http://www.theenergycollective.com/charlesbarton/49358/jacobson-beyond-cherry-picking

[21] http://quotesgram.com/dwight-eisenhower-quotes-on-planning/

[22] https://evernote.com

[23] http://www.ans.org/pi/news/article-514/

[24] http://thebreakthrough.org

[25] http://atomicinsights.com/the-three-gorges-dam-why-china-is-run-by-engineers/

[26] Meredith Angwin, "All Around the Coal Boiler", February 11th, 2010, http://yesvy.blogspot.com/2010/02/all-around-coal-boiler.html#.Vz 7skjZfD3E

[27] https://www.eia.gov/electricity/monthly/epm_table_grapher.cfm?t= epmt_6_07_a

[28] https://en.wikipedia.org/wiki/Fossil-fuel_power_station#Radioactive_trace_elements

[29] http://www.nrc.gov/about-nrc/radiation/related-info/faq.html#9

[30] http://www.nrc.gov/about-nrc/radiation/around-us/doses-daily-lives.html

[31] http://www.physics.isu.edu/radinf/risk.htm

[32] http://www.nrc.gov/about-nrc/radiation/around-us/calculator.html

33 James Conca, "How Deadly Is Your Kilowatt? We Rank The Killer Energy Sources," *Forbes*, June 10th, 2012, http://www.forbes.com/sites/jamesconca/2012/06/10/energys-deathprint-a-price-always-paid/#1339d25149d2

34 http://journals.plos.org/plosone/articl?id=10.1371/journal.pone.0143611

35 Geoffrey A. Fowler, "When the Most Personal Secrets Get Outed on Facebook," *Wall Street Journal*, October 13, 2012, http://www.wsj.com/articles/SB10000872396390444165804578008740578200224

36 Meredith Angwin, "My Comment to the NRC in favor of abandoning LNT and ALARA for rule making," August 28th, 2015, http://yesvy.blogspot.com/2015/08/my-comment-to-nrc-in-favor-of.html

37 http://canadianenergyissues.com

38 http://atomicinsights.com/atomic-show-252-security-future-energy-heu/

39 http://www.npr.org/2013/03/11/174027294/the-nasty-effect-how-comments-color-comprehension?ft=1&f=1007

40 James Conca, "How Deadly Is Your Kilowatt? We Rank The Killer Energy Sources," *Forbes*, June 10th, 2012, http://www.forbes.com/sites/jamesconca/2012/06/10/energys-deathprint-a-price-always-paid/#593 630b949d2

41 https://www.nih.gov/news-events/news-releases/elevated-bladder-cancer-risk-new-england-arsenic-drinking-water-private-wells

42 https://en.wikipedia.org/wiki/Three_Mile_Island_accident_health_effects#cite_note-nih1-6

43 http://www.unscear.org/unscear/en/chernobyl.html

44 https://en.wikipedia.org/wiki/Chernobyl_Exclusion_Zone

45 George Johnson, "The Nuclear Tourist," *National Geographic*, October 2014, http://ngm.nationalgeographic.com/2014/10/nuclear-tourism/johnson-text.

46 http://www.world-nuclear.org/information-library/safety-and-security/safety-of-plants/chernobyl-accident.aspx

47 https://en.wikipedia.org/wiki/Chernobyl_Nuclear_Power_Plant

48 https://en.wikipedia.org/wiki/Chernobyl_Forum

49 http://www.unscear.org/unscear/en/chernobyl.html

50 http://www.world-nuclear.org/information-library/safety-and-security/safety-of-plants/chernobyl-accident.aspx

51 http://www.ncbi.nlm.nih.gov/pmc/articles/PMC3487052/

52 http://www.world-nuclear.org/information-library/safety-and-security/safety-of-plants/fukushima-accident.aspx

53 http://nextbigfuture.com/2014/02/evacuation-deaths-in-japan-in-2011-were.html

54 https://en.wikipedia.org/wiki/Fukushima_Daiichi_Nuclear_Power_Plant

55 https://hbr.org/2014/07/how-the-other-fukushima-plant-survived

56 https://www.theguardian.com/world/2011/mar/30/onagawa-tsunami-refugees-nuclear-plant

57 http://www.hiroshimasyndrome.com/fukushima-accident-updates.html

58 http://www.who.int/mediacentre/news/releases/2013/fukushima_report_20130228/en/

59 Wade Allison, *Radiation and Reason* (York Publishing Services: 2009), http://www.radiationandreason.com

60 http://atomicinsights.com/radiation-safe-within-limits-robert-hargraves/

61 http://yesvy.blogspot.com/2011/05/nimby-and-nukes-vermont-utility-makes.html#.Vs49HjZdL3E

62 www.mailchimp.com; www.constantcontact.com

63 http://aplacetogive.scouting.org

64 http://nssavannahdocumentary.com

65 http://www.guidestar.org/Home.aspx

66 http://www.brainyquote.com/quotes/quotes/i/isaacnewto395010.html

67 https://en.wikipedia.org/wiki/L%27esprit_de_l%27escalier

68 https://en.wikipedia.org/wiki/Pirkei_Avot

69 http://www.nrel.gov/docs/fy09osti/45834.pdf

70 http://www.withouthotair.com

71 http://shrinkthatfootprint.com/average-household-electricity-consumption

72 Meredith Angwin, "The 90% Solution: What 90% Renewables Would Look Like in Vermont," May 14th, 2013, http://yesvy.blogspot.com/2013/05/the-90-solution-what-90-renewables.html#.VwW7mDam73E

73 Jim Conca, "The Biggest Power Plants in America—Not What You Think," *Forbes,* April 20th, 2015, http://www.forbes.com/sites/jamesconca/2015/04/20/the-ten-biggest-power-plants-in-america-not-what-everyone-claims/#33f2a2122107

[74] Meredith Angwin, "Atoms Not Dams. Surprising Facts for Earth Day," April 22nd, 2015, http://yesvy.blogspot.com/2015/04/atoms-not-dams-surprising-facts-for.html#.Vy-lmjam73E

[75] http://www.cgnp.org

[76] http://ansnuclearcafe.org/2012/09/11/great-turnout-at-moxchat/

[77] Ethan Allen Institute, "Huge Crowd Rejects Vermont's Renewable Energy Policies," no date, http://ethanallen.org/huge-crowd-rejects-vermonts-renewable-energy-policies/; Rod Adams, "NRC and Army Corps of Engineers Joint Public Meeting—Draft Environmental Impact Statement for Calvert Cliffs Unit 3," May 26th, 2010, http://atomicinsights.com/nrc-and-army-corps-of-engineers-joint-public-meeting-draft-environmental-impact-statement-for-calvert-cliffs-unit-3/

[78] Rod Adams, "Supporters of Nuclear Energy Development Face Off with Antinuclear Activists in Gaffney," Atomic Insights, January 20th, 2012, http://atomicinsights.com/supporters-of-nuclear-energy-development-face-off-with-antinuclear-activists-in-gaffney-sc/

[79] George Angwin and Meredith Angwin, *Voices of Vermont Yankee* (Carnot Communications: 2013), http://www.amazon.com/Voices-Vermont-Yankee-George-Angwin-ebook/dp/B00BJ7KSTQ

[80] Richard Trudell, "Baseball, Reliable Power, and Vermont Yankee: Richard Trudell Guest Post," November 14th, 2012, http://yesvy.blogspot.com/2012/11/baseball-reliable-power-and-vermont.html#.Vq1hbDZMk-0

[81] Nuclear Energy Institute, "Price-Anderson Act Provides Effective Liability Insurance at No Cost to the Public," March 2014, http://www.nei.org/Master-Document-Folder/Backgrounders/Fact-Sheets/Insurance-Price-Anderson-Act-Provides-Effective-Li

[82] http://www.amazon.com/Voices-Vermont-Yankee-George-Angwin-ebook/dp/B00BJ7KSTQ

[83] http://ansnuclearcafe.org/2012/05/29/nrc-public-meeting-in-brattleboro/

[84] Meredith Angwin, "Speaking Out of Turn at the NRC Meeting," *ANS Nuclear Café*, May 2nd, 2013, http://ansnuclearcafe.org/2013/05/02/speaking-out-of-turn-at-nrc-meeting/

[85] Dale Carnegie, *How to Win Friends and Influence People*, (New York: Simon & Schuster, 2010), http://www.amazon.com/s/ref=nb_sb_ss_i_1_7?url=search-alias%3Ddigital-text&field-keywords=how+to+win+friends+and+influence+people&sprefix=how+to+%2Cdigital-text%2C138

86 Kerry Patterson, *Crucial Conversations: Tools for Talking When Stakes Are High* (New York: McGraw-Hill, 2011), https://itunes.apple.com/us/book/crucial-conversations/id502458523?mt=11

87 http://www.dropeik.com/dropeik/index.html; David Ropeik, "The Great Zika Freak-Out. A Teaching Moment in the Psychology of Fear," *Huffington Post*, January 29th, 2016, http://www.huffingtonpost.com/david-ropeik/the-great-zika-freak-out_b_9112978.html

88 http://cravenspowertosavetheworld.com.

89 http://www.prnewswire.com

90 https://www.helpareporter.com

91 http://www.eia.gov/todayinenergy/detail.cfm?id=14011

92 https://en.wikipedia.org/wiki/Paris_Agreement

93 World Nuclear Association, "The Nuclear Renaissance," September 2015, http://www.world-nuclear.org/information-library/current-and-future-generation/the-nuclear-renaissance.aspx

94 http://visualoop.com/infographics/without-electricity-1-3-billion-are-living-in-the-dark

95 https://www.eia.gov/todayinenergy/detail.cfm?id=14011

96 Meredith Angwin, "A Book I Loved: THORIUM: Energy Cheaper Than Coal by Bob Hargraves," August 28th, 2012, http://yesvy.blogspot.com/2012/08/a-book-i-loved-thorium-energy-cheaper.html#.VwZW_jam73E

97 http://www.ted.com/talks/hans_rosling_and_the_magic_washing_machine?language=en

98 Meredith Angwin, "The Oversold Smart Grid: Dismissing the Work of Women," April 7th, 2013, http://yesvy.blogspot.com/2013/04/the-oversold-smart-grid-dismissing-work.html#.Vy_EHjam73E

99 World Nuclear Association, "Uranium, Electricity, and Climate Change," December 2012, http://www.world-nuclear.org/information-library/energy-and-the-environment/uranium,-electricity-and-climate-change.aspx

100 World Nuclear Association, "Plans for New Reactors Worldwide," April 2016, http://www.world-nuclear.org/information-library/current-and-future-generation/plans-for-new-reactors-worldwide.aspx

101 http://www.c-n-t-a.com

102 https://physical-sciences.uchicago.edu/page/climate-change-101%E2%80%94and-beyond

103 http://www.nuclearscienceweek.org/about-nsw/

104 https://en.wikipedia.org/wiki/Edward_Tufte

105 Edward R. Tufte, *The Visual Display of Quantitative Information* (Cheshire, CT: Graphics Press, 2001), http://www.amazon.com/Visual-Display-Quantitative-Information/dp/0961392142

106 Meredith Angwin, "Asthma Society of Canada Testimony in Favor of Relicensing Bruce Power," November 26th, 2015, http://yesvy.blogspot .com/2015/11/asthma-society-of-canada-testimony-in.html

107 (https://upload.wikimedia.org/wikipedia/commons/2/29/Minard.png)

108 Meredith Angwin, "Why Do They Listen to Alvarez?" http://northwest cleanenergy.com/2014/11/20/why-do-they-listen-to-alvarez/

109 Meredith Angwin, "Asthma Society of Canada Testimony in Favor of Relicensing Bruce Power," November 26th, 2015, http://yesvy.blogspot .com/2015/11/asthma-society-of-canada-testimony-in.html#.

110 http://www.nytimes.com/2014/12/21/world/asia/fuel-rods-are-removed-from-japans-damaged-fukushima-reactor.html?_r=0

111 http://www.snopes.com/photos/technology/fukushima.asp

112 http://boingboing.net/2011/06/23/fukushima-babies-and.html

113 Meredith Angwin, "Chernobyl and the Montshire Museum," March 11th, 2010, http://yesvy.blogspot.com/2010/02/chernobyl-and-montshire-museum.html#.

114 Duke Energy, "The Powerful Art of PopAtomic Studios," June 28th, 2011, http://nuclear.duke-energy.com/2011/06/28/the-powerful-art-of-popatomic-studios/

115 http://yesvy.blogspot.com/2011/09/rally-retrospective-on-sidewalks-for.html#.VqKW4TZMk-0

116 http://ansnuclearcafe.org/2011/09/27/rally-for-nuclear-power-and-vermont-yankee/

117 http://www.neimagazine.com

INDEX

ABOUT CAMPAIGNING FOR CLEAN AIR: STRATEGIES FOR PRO-NUCLEAR ADVOCACY

In *Campaigning for Clean Air*, award-winning Meredith Angwin describes how to be an effective pro-nuclear supporter. She provides practical help and real-life examples for many different levels of advocacy. The book contains media-savvy hints for writing letters to the editor (activism from behind your computer). It includes guidelines for organizing pro-nuclear demonstrations (activism on the street). And everything in between!

Healthy, safe, and secure lives depend on reliable energy. Nuclear power plants produce steady, abundant electricity: low-carbon and low-pollution. Help move the world to a clean-air future. Enjoy reading this book, and enjoy your nuclear advocacy!

ABOUT THE AUTHOR

Photo by Tom McNeill

MEREDITH ANGWIN HAS AN M.S. in physical chemistry from the University of Chicago. In her long research career, she was inventor on several patents in pollution control for fossil fuels and did extensive work in corrosion control for nuclear plants. Meredith was one of the first women to be a project manager at EPRI (Electric Power Research Institute). In recent years, she has devoted herself to being an advocate for clean, safe nuclear energy. For her outreach work, she was a recipient of a President's Citation award from the American Nuclear Society. She publishes at her own blog, as a guest blogger, and in several magazines.

Meredith leads workshops and gives presentations on effective pro-nuclear advocacy. Contact her at mjangwin@gmail.com.

CPSIA information can be obtained
at www.ICGtesting.com
Printed in the USA
FFOW01n0053100517
35417FF